God Made
LIFE

WORKBOOK

EDITORS

Kevin Swanson and Kayla White

Generations

PASSING ON THE FAITH

1st Printing, July 2021.

Printed in the United States of America.

ISBN: 978-1-954745-27-8

Cover Design: Justin Turley
Interior Design: Sarah Lee Bryant

Cover Image: Baby sucking thumb at 20 weeks. LENNART NILSSON, TT/SCIENCE PHOTO LIBRARY. Used by permission.

Published by:
Generations
19039 Plaza Drive Ste 210
Parker, Colorado 80134
Generations.org

For more information on this and other titles from Generations,
visit Generations.org or call (888) 389-9080.

TABLE OF CONTENTS

COURSE INTRODUCTION

Make a joyful shout to the LORD, all you lands!
Serve the LORD with gladness;
Come before His presence with singing.
Know that the LORD, He is God;
It is He who has made us, and not we ourselves;
We are His people and the sheep of His pasture.
Enter into His gates with thanksgiving,
And into His courts with praise.
Be thankful to Him, and bless His name.
For the LORD is good;
His mercy is everlasting,
And His truth endures to all generations. (Psalm 100)

This course is intended to produce a paradigm shift in the way that this generation of Christian children understand science. Differing worldviews must yield radically different approaches to science. The method of study, the purpose for the study, and the content of the study will vary greatly. A biblical worldview perspective of science always puts God at the center. God is personal, and He is the source of all things. His fingerprints are all over this wide world. All knowledge of His creation must constantly reveal His power and glory unless great pains are taken to willfully and continually suppress this truth. Thus, the student of the natural world should find this course always delighting in the revelation of God's genius wisdom, power, and goodness—everywhere manifest. Let us maximize on the great purpose for all of life. Indeed, the purpose of science is to enjoy God in the context of His creation and praise Him for His marvelous works!

The study of science is deeply personal because it is revelatory of the personality of God. These are not random accidents in a chance universe. These are all the careful design of a personal, loving, wise, and all-powerful Creator. We want the student fully engaged, rejoicing in, delighting in, praising, and thanking God for the awesomeness and manifold blessings of His creation!

Throughout, we will glory in the incomparable wisdom of God! It is with an effervescent delight that we boast of God's genius—one million times more intricate, more complex, more wonderful, than anything man has ever made. Here is the highest of the material creation—the creation of life! We are not afraid to say that we can't explain this or that. We cheerfully let the student know that the greatest scientists in the world cannot comprehend the deep mysteries of God's wisdom in this creation. We fall on our faces in awe-filled worship! This is the only way to avoid the academic pride, the scientific hubris, and the lack of the fear of God that has ruined science and education in a humanist age.

This course also provides extensive devotional reading from Scripture throughout, since all Christian education must retain the Word of God as "a frontlet" before our eyes and our children's eyes (Deut. 6:7-9). We offer many opportunities for prayer and the singing of praise. These elements are core to a Christian view of science. As the teacher/parent disciples the child in the study of God's creation, we hope and pray that the student will form a Godward view of science and all of life.

If education will be truly effective, the student must be constantly made aware of the vital purpose of this study. Hardly a page of the text should go by without the student realizing the significance and purpose of the study. For the Christian, the purpose of science is absolutely clear. It is for praise and worship and for taking right dominion as good stewards over God's world. We will glory in His nature and His works, and we seek to fulfill our role in ruling over the natural world (as the Lord commanded man to do at the beginning).

If there is a clear integration of praise and life application on every page, the material will be much better retained. Perpetually spewing out disconnected and purposeless facts into a child's brain does little for retention. When science instruction is given meaning and purpose on every page of the text, in every minute of the class, the student will be much more likely retain the material and apply it in a meaningful way in his life.

The "Do" sections contained at the end of each chapter are not intended to serve as the typical "laboratory" experience or hypothetical exercises. Rather, these are intended to serve as real life application for the science conveyed in the chapter. We want the students to actually practice the science they learn for the real benefit of their family, their community, and their personal economy. Although many of the practical projects suggested are simple and easy, we would recommend taking on only one *major* project for the academic year. Teacher and parent involvement is highly recommended for these projects.

This student workbook also includes observational experiments to be conducted during the assigned week, as laid out in the lesson schedule.

For 6th-8th grade level students, Generations here introduces a biblical worldview into basic biology in the most winsome way possible. Captured in this introduction to science are the most amazing facts and the most interesting facets of God's creation. Efforts are made to explain difficult concepts at a 10 to 12-year-old level, without losing the substance of the scientific meaning. It was our goal that not a paragraph be uninteresting, vague, or too difficult.

The text crosses over from the theoretical to the applicable and meaningful by drawing in discussions on diseases, medical treatments, nutrition, and health. Yet, the goal is always to point the students back to our sovereign God in right reverence and worship. Then we offer helpful, relevant, and interesting life (and spiritual) applications for each disastrous scenario—preparing each young student to respond rightly (in faith, wisdom, and faithful stewardship) to these amazing works of our Creator God.

THIS STUDENT WORKBOOK INCLUDES

1. Lesson Schedule

2. Study Questions

3. Scripture Exercises

4. Spiritual Life Application Questions

5. Hands-on Science Projects

6. Answer Key

COURSE OBJECTIVES

This course is dedicated to the glory of God and to the preeminence of the Lord Jesus Christ in all things. The essential objectives for the course must therefore be:

1. That all who study this course would give God the glory for His sovereignty, His power, His goodness, His wisdom, His judgments, and His mercy.

2. That our children would come to know God in His works.

3. That our children would realize that Jesus Christ is the Creator of all things and by Him all things consist.

4. That our children would recognize that the Lord Jesus Christ is preeminent in all things, and by Him all of these biological systems exist.

5. That our children would immediately realize the purpose for science on every page and in every lesson—to glorify God, and to wisely and obediently rule over the animal creation.

6. That our children will learn to integrate the knowledge they obtain of God's world into life.

7. That our children would know Scripture better and see its amazing relevance to every part of life (including science), especially as the passages are meditated upon throughout the course.

8. That our children would learn to be more grateful and more ready to give God the praise and the glory for His goodness to us.

TEACHING METHOD

In order for this course to have maximum effect, the teacher/parent should:

1. Realize the joy and excitement of exploring God's world,

2. Love God,

3. Seek to learn more of the awesomeness of God manifested in His creative work, and share that enthusiasm with the children,

4. Accept the obligation to follow through on knowledge by real life application. This curriculum and lesson schedule is laid out in a carefully-designed manner, such that the lesson culminates in praise and practical life application.

The following presents the order of the learning process:

1. Read the material.

2. Pray, sing, and worship God.

3. Watch excellently-produced videos to better understand the material.

4. Study the important vocabulary terms used in the chapter.

5. Answer study questions and review Bible passages.

6. Make spiritual life application.

7. Observe through experimentation.

8. Take dominion using the "Do" projects contained in the textbook.

Almost every chapter in the text includes real-life application exercises along with the hands-on experiments contained in this workbook. Some of these exercises will be more time-intensive than others. Select the more time-intensive exercise carefully, and we would only recommend one to two time-intensive exercises for each of the "Do" projects and the "Hands-on" experiments.

The parent/teacher may consider reading the material out loud. The text is designed to be engaging to children of all ages as well as adults.

LESSON SCHEDULE

The lesson schedule is provided as a suggestion—teachers/parents and students may adapt the schedule to suit their needs. The lesson schedule is based on a 36-week school year divided into two semesters.

COMPLETING CHAPTER ASSIGNMENTS

While reading the text, the student should carefully consider all of the Scriptures provided. The Scriptures provide the most essential elements of knowledge by which we understand God's world. The key terms and animal designations are emboldened. The students should pay close attention to these as they will be referred to in the study questions and exam. Upon completion of reading, students may complete the chapter assignments open-book.

GRADING CHAPTER ASSIGNMENTS

The teacher/parent may determine for themselves how they would grade the assignments. The following is recommended:

The workbook exercises are best suited for grading. Provide one point for each of the numbered exercises, excluding the Spiritual Application (at the end of each lesson). For each chapter assignment, divide the total number of questions answered correctly with the total number of questions possible to calculate the percentage.

For example, if 8 out of 11 questions were correct, then the percentage grade for that assignment will be 72% (8/11=72%). If the student receives less than 90% correct answers, it is highly recommended that he/she reread the chapter and make corrections for the questions missed.

GRADING PROJECTS

It is recommended that the projects be graded on the basis of completion or participation. If the student completed the experiment or project, he gets 100% for that project. If he left the project only half complete, he gets 0% for that experiment or project. If the student completed three quarters of the project, he should receive a 75% grade.

FINAL COURSE GRADE VALUES

To calculate the final course grade, the parent/teacher may use the following recommended weighted score:

- Completion of experiments and projects assigned = 50%
- Study questions = 40%
- Final Exam = 10%

- Final Grade = 0.50 x (average score for experiments/projects) + 0.40 x (average score on lessons) + 0.10 x (final exam score)

- 90-100% = A
- 80-89% = B
- 70-79% = C
- 60-69% = D
- 0-59% = F

The Generations Curriculum Team

July 2021, AD

First Semester Suggested Daily Schedule

Date	Day	Assignment	Due Date	✔	Grade
First Semester—First Quarter					
Week 1	1	Read Chapter 1, pages 7-13			
	2				
	3	Read Chapter 1, pages 13-17			
	4				
	5	Read Chapter 1, pages 17-23			
Week 2	1	Complete Chapter 1 Worksheet, Vocabulary			
	2				
	3	Complete Chapter 1 Worksheet, Comprehension Questions			
	4				
	5	Complete Chapter 1 Worksheet, Faith Lessons			
Week 3	1	Complete Chapter 1 Worksheet, Hands-on Science			
	2				
	3	Complete Chapter 1, "Do" Exercise			
	4				
	5				
Week 4	1	Read Chapter 2, pages 27-32			
	2				
	3	Read Chapter 2, pages 32-39			
	4				
	5	Complete Chapter 2 Worksheet, Part I			

Date	Day	Assignment	Due Date	✔	Grade
Week 5	1	Read Chapter 2, pages 39-45			
	2				
	3	Read Chapter 2, pages 45-50			
	4				
	5	Complete Chapter 2 Worksheet, Part II			
Week 6	1	Complete Chapter 2 Worksheet, Hands-on Science			
	2				
	3	Complete Chapter 2, "Do" Exercise			
	4				
	5				
Week 7	1	Read Chapter 3, pages 59-65			
	2				
	3	Read Chapter 3, pages 65-69			
	4				
	5	Complete Chapter 3 Worksheet, Part I			
Week 8	1	Read Chapter 3, pages 69-75			
	2				
	3	Read Chapter 3, pages 75-78			
	4				
	5	Complete Chapter 3 Worksheet, Part II			
Week 9	1	Complete Chapter 3 Worksheet, Hands-on Science			
	2				
	3	Complete Chapter 3, "Do" Exercise			
	4				
	5				

Date	Day	Assignment	Due Date	✔	Grade
First Semester-Second Quarter					
Week 10	1	Read Chapter 4, pages 83-93			
	2				
	3	Read Chapter 4, pages 93-101			
	4				
	5	Complete Chapter 4 Worksheet, Part I			
Week 11	1	Read Chapter 4, pages 101-106			
	2				
	3	Read Chapter 4, pages 107-113			
	4				
	5	Complete Chapter 4 Worksheet, Part II			
Week 12	1	Complete Chapter 4 Worksheet, Hands-on Science			
	2				
	3				
	4				
	5				
Week 13	1	Complete Chapter 4 Worksheet, "Do" Exercise			
	2				
	3				
	4				
	5				
Week 14	1	Read Chapter 5, pages 119-126			
	2				
	3	Read Chapter 5, pages 127-132			
	4				
	5	Complete Chapter 5 Worksheet, Part I			

Date	Day	Assignment	Due Date	✔	Grade
Week 15	1	Read Chapter 5, pages 132-140			
	2				
	3	Read Chapter 5, pages 141-148			
	4				
	5	Complete Chapter 5 Worksheet, Part II			
Week 16	1	Complete Chapter 5 Worksheet, Hands-on Science			
	2				
	3				
	4				
	5				
Week 17	1	Complete Chapter 5, "Do" Exercise			
	2				
	3				
	4				
	5				
Week 18	1	Read Chapter 6, pages 155-165			
	2				
	3	Read Chapter 6, pages 165-171			
	4				
	5	Read Chapter 6, pages 171-174			
			Mid-Term Grade		

Second Semester Suggested Daily Schedule

Date	Day	Assignment	Due Date	✔	Grade
		Second Semester—Third Quarter			
Week 19	1	Read Chapter 6, pages 175-178			
	2				
	3	Read Chapter 6, pages 178-183			
	4				
	5	Complete Chapter 6 Worksheet			
Week 20	1	Complete Chapter 6 Worksheet, Hands-on Science			
	2				
	3	Complete Chapter 6, "Do" Exercise			
	4				
	5				
Week 21	1	Read Chapter 7, pages 187-194			
	2				
	3	Read Chapter 7, pages 194-199			
	4				
	5	Complete Chapter 7 Worksheet, Part I			
Week 22	1	Read Chapter 7, pages 199-207			
	2				
	3	Read Chapter 7, pages 207-216			
	4				
	5	Complete Chapter 7 Worksheet, Part II			
Week 23	1	Complete Chapter 7 Worksheet, Hands-on Science			
	2				
	3				
	4				
	5				

Date	Day	Assignment	Due Date	✔	Grade
Week 24	1	Complete Chapter 7, "Do" Exercise			
	2				
	3				
	4				
	5				
Week 25	1	Read Chapter 8, pages 221-229			
	2				
	3	Read Chapter 8, pages 230-237			
	4				
	5	Complete Chapter 8 Worksheet, Part I			
Week 26	1	Read Chapter 8, pages 237-243			
	2				
	3	Read Chapter 8, pages 243-251			
	4				
	5	Complete Chapter 8 Worksheet, Part II			
Week 27	1	Complete Chapter 8 Worksheet, Hands-on Science			
	2				
	3				
	4				
	5				

Date	Day	Assignment	Due Date	✔	Grade
		Second Semester—Fourth Quarter			
Week 28	1	Complete Chapter 8, "Do" Exercise			
	2				
	3				
	4				
	5				
Week 29	1	Read Chapter 9, pages 257-262			
	2				
	3	Read Chapter 9, pages 262-270			
	4				
	5	Complete Chapter 9 Worksheet, Part I			
Week 30	1	Read Chapter 9, pages 270-274			
	2				
	3	Read Chapter 9, pages 274-280			
	4				
	5	Complete Chapter 9 Worksheet, Part II			
Week 31	1	Complete Chapter 9 Worksheet, Hands-on Science			
	2				
	3	Complete Chapter 9, "Do" Exercise			
	4				
	5				
Week 32	1	Read Chapter 10, pages 285-292			
	2				
	3	Read Chapter 10, pages 292-296			
	4				
	5	Complete Chapter 10 Worksheet, Part I			

Date	Day	Assignment	Due Date	✔	Grade
Week 33	1	Read Chapter 10, pages 296-304			
	2				
	3	Read Chapter 10, pages 304-313			
	4				
	5	Complete Chapter 10 Worksheet, Part II			
Week 34	1	Complete Chapter 10, "Do" Exercise			
	2				
	3				
	4				
	5				
Week 35	1	Complete Final Exam			
	2				
	3				
	4				
	5				
Week 36	1				
	2				
	3				
	4				
	5				
				Final Grade	

Chapter 1
WHAT IS TRUE?

VOCABULARY

Match each of the following terms with the correct description.

Hypothesis

Experiment

Observe

Origins

Fossils

Microbiologist

Confounding

Anesthesia

Extinct

Confusing

Drugs or gases that will desensitize a person to pain

A certain species of animal that died out and there are none left anywhere in the world today

A scientist who studies tiny creatures

A study of how the world began or how life began

To test a scientific hypothesis or theory

The remains or form of an animal cast in rock (usually by water)

To watch or to study God's creation

A scientific guess that needs to be confirmed by experiments

COMPREHENSION QUESTIONS

1. What are the sorts of things science cannot do?

_____

_____

_____

2. Is the moon made out of cheese? How do we know for sure?

_____

_____

3. How would you test this theory: _Leaves on trees turn yellow and brown in the autumn or winter because of the colder temperatures._

_____

_____

_____

_____

4. How does a rock differ from a human being? Name at least two differences.

_____

_____

_____

5. How can you become more certain about your scientific theories? List the five points provided in your text.

a. _____

b. _____

c. _____

d. _____

e. _____

6. What is the problem with encyclopedias and experts?

_____

_____

_____

7. When did God give the following important inventions?

_____ Pastor Cotton Mather of Boston, Massachusetts, discovered the smallpox vaccine.

_____ Anesthesia was first discovered by several dentists in America.

_____ A French microbiologist named Louis Pasteur figured out that germs cause bad diseases.

_____ The X-ray was accidentally discovered by a Christian physicist named Wilhelm Conrad Röntgen.

_____ The first antibiotic was discovered by Christian researcher Alexander Fleming.

_____ A Christian inventor named Raymond Damadian developed Magnetic Resonance Imaging.

8. Name two "scientists" who confused history for science.

_____

_____

9. Why were Lyell's theories so hard to believe? What were the things he assumed before he produced his theories?

_____

_____

_____

10. What was the big problem with Darwin's theories?

_____

_____

_____

11. What would scientists have to do in order to prove evolution?

_____

_____

_____

12. What are the oldest writings discovered?

_____

_____

13. What was the most important event that took place in all of world history?

_____

14. How do we know for sure that a worldwide flood happened about 2518 BC?

_____

_____

FAITH LESSONS

1. Read the following verse. Why is God's Word more trustworthy than the teachings of evolutionists?

> The words of the LORD are pure words,
> Like silver tried in a furnace of earth,
> Purified seven times. (Psalm 12:6)

_____

_____

_____

2. Abraham told the rich man in the parable: "'If [your brothers] do not hear Moses and the prophets, neither will they be persuaded though one rise from the dead.'" (Luke 16:31)

Why do some people refuse to read or to listen to Moses and the prophets?

_____

_____

Why would some people not listen to somebody who rises from the dead?

_____

_____

3. Study Genesis 7:1-4, 18-24. Based on God's Word, how can we know for sure that the flood covered the whole world?

_____

_____

_____

HANDS-ON SCIENCE

1. Perform an experiment to test the following hypotheses:

Hypothesis # —Bleach will kill weeds (or a certain plant).

Hypothesis #2—A certain kind of manure will help weeds (or a certain plant) to grow

Obtain three sets of weeds or small plants. Keep them planted in dirt, and be sure they have access to sunlight.

Pour ¼ cup of bleach on the first set of weeds/plants every day for four days.

Place fresh animal manure around the second set of weeds/plants. Mix it into the dirt a little bit.

Don't do anything special for the third set of weeds/plants.

The first two groups are your **experimental groups**. The third group is your **control group**.

Be sure that all three sets of plants have the same amount of sunlight and be sure they get the same amount of water. Monitor the condition of the plants for two weeks.

Compare the health of each of the three sets of weeds/plants at the end of the first and second week.

Was Hypothesis #1 confirmed as true or not? How sure are you of this conclusion?

_____

_____

_____

Was Hypothesis #2 confirmed as true or not? How sure are you of this conclusion?

_____

_____

_____

2. Perform an experiment to test the following hypotheses:

    Hypothesis #1—A milk chocolate bar stays hard at 68-75°F (20-24°C).

    Hypothesis #2—A milk chocolate bar melts above 90-95°F (32-35°C).

    Place a milk chocolate bar on a plate at room temperature 68-75°F (20-24°C) for 15-20 minutes.

    Place a milk chocolate bar on a plate in an oven at 90-95°F (32-35°C) for 15-20 minutes.

    Was Hypothesis #1 confirmed as true or not? How sure are you of this conclusion?

    _____

    _____

    _____

    Was Hypothesis #2 confirmed as true or not? How sure are you of this conclusion?

    _____

    _____

    _____

LIFE APPLICATION

Complete the **Pray**, **Sing**, and **Watch** sections of the chapter.

Chapter 2

WHAT IS LIFE?

PART I

Covers reading material from the beginning of the chapter up to The Raw Materials of the Cell

VOCABULARY

Match each of the following terms with the correct description.

Abiogenesis	The most basic, self-contained building block of life
Isopropyl alcohol	Creatures that live off of dead organisms
Cytoplasm	Breaks down fats and carbs for cell energy
Anabolism	Cells without organelles
Catabolism	Organisms like plants that make their own food
Enzymes	The idea that life can come from non-life—something like a rock turning into a human being
Photosynthesis	Little organs found in cells
Producers	Proteins used to get chemical reactions going in your body
Consumers	The inside of a cell except for the nucleus
Decomposers	Cells with organelles
Ecosystem	Creatures that eat plants and animals
Cell	Rubbing alcohol
Prokaryotic cell	The method plants use to make their own food
Eukaryotic cell	Takes useful carbs, fats, and proteins for the body from food
Organelles	All the living and non-living parts of a community

COMPREHENSION QUESTIONS

1. What are the two purposes for this course?

   _____

   _____

   _____

2. What two characteristics does the Bible use to define life or "higher life forms"?

   _____

   _____

   _____

3. What is the hierarchy of life from the highest to the lowest?

   _____

   _____

   _____

4. How are animals different from humans?

   _____

   _____

   _____

5. Fill in the following blanks:

   Biology: The study of _____

   Microbiology: The study of _____

   Zoology: The study of _____

   Botany: The study of _____

   Anatomy: The study of the _____

   Physiology: The study of the _____

6. What are the seven characteristics of organisms? Fill in the following blanks.

   Organisms are made of _____.

   Man and animals all experience the sad reality of _____.

   Organisms _____.

   Organisms need food for _____.

   Cell-based organisms _____.

   Organisms start out very small as a single cell or a seed, and they _____.

   Organisms react to outside _____.

7. What is the most important source of energy that provides food for plants, for animals, and for man?

   _____

   _____

8. What kind of cells was Robert Hooke looking at in 1665 when he discovered the cell? Were they plant or animal cells?

   _____

   _____

9. Is the human body made out of eukaryotic or prokaryotic cells?

   _____

10. What are the seven basic processes of the cell?

   _____

   _____

   _____

   _____

FAITH LESSONS

1. How did God create man according to Genesis 2:7?

_____

_____

2. Review Genesis 3. How did death come into the world?

_____

_____

3. Read John 6:33 and John 11:25-26. What is the source of life?

_____

_____

4. Consider Isaiah 30:23-24. How does the prophet trace every blessing to God?

_____

_____

Then He will give the rain for your seed
With which you sow the ground,
And bread of the increase of the earth;
It will be fat and plentiful.
In that day your cattle will feed
In large pastures.
Likewise the oxen and the young donkeys that work the ground
Will eat cured fodder,
Which has been winnowed with the shovel and fan. (Isaiah 30:23-24)

PART II

Covers reading material from The Raw Materials of the Cell *to the end of the chapter*

VOCABULARY

Match each of the following terms with the correct description.

Glucose

Glycogen globules

Amino acids

Organic compounds

Catalyst

Larvae

DNA

RNA

Ions

Myosin

Cytoskeleton

Flagellum

Cilia

Irreducible complexity

Cancer

Metastasis

Substances made of carbon

Atoms with more electrons than protons, or more protons than electrons

The condition when cancerous cells are spreading through the body

Early stages of insects

Finger-like things that can move the cell along

The cell's basic food—a kind of carbohydrate

A disease that consists of old cells or bad cells in the body reproducing and creating tumors

When lots of things need to work in order for the system to work

A little tail on a cell that helps it move along

Your body stores glucose in this form

Helps build proteins by carrying the blueprint instructions outside of the nucleus to other parts of the cell

The building blocks for proteins

The bones and muscles of a cell

A protein that gets things moving in the cell

The blueprints or instructions for making proteins (and all living things)

Something that triggers a chemical reaction

COMPREHENSION QUESTIONS

1. What is the largest cell in God's creation? How many human cells could you fit on the head of a pin?

_____

_____

2. Of what kind of materials are houses made?

_____

_____

What kinds of raw materials did God use to create the human body?

_____

_____

List the percentage of each of the following materials found in the human body:

Water: _____%

Fat: _____%

Protein: _____%

Minerals: _____%

Carbohydrates: _____%

3. List three things proteins can do.

a. _____

b. _____

c. _____

4. What basic element is found in every amino acid?

_____

5. How did the maggots help the healing process when soldiers were wounded?

_____

_____

6. What is the difference between the DNA and the RNA?

_____

_____

7. How are cells different from man-produced cars?

_____

_____

_____

8. List at least five things that have to work in order for the little flagellum motor to work.

_____

_____

_____

_____

_____

9. What is the difference between a bird's beak growing a little longer through evolution, and a flagellum developing by evolution?

_____

_____

_____

10. Scientists are pretty sure that what two things cause cancer?

_____

_____

11. What are the things that scientists are pretty sure prevent cancer?

_____

_____

FAITH LESSONS

1. Read Job 38:1-7. This universe is very complicated. List at least five things we do not understand about the universe—the cell, the stars, light, the atom, etc. What should be our response to all of this?

_____

_____

_____

2. Study Romans 1:21-22. How do proud scientists and others become fools? List the steps covered in these verses.

_____

_____

_____

_____

HANDS-ON SCIENCE

DNA from a Banana

Objective: To visually examine DNA molecules extracted from a banana.

Note: For a visual presentation of this experiment, you may watch an online video entitled "Banana DNA Experiment" with adult supervision.

Materials Needed:

Half of a ripe banana

1/2 cup hot water

1 tsp salt

1/2 tsp liquid dishwashing soap

Resealable zipped plastic bag (quart size)

Cold isopropyl alcohol (rubbing alcohol) from freezer

1 coffee filter

A clear, glass container

Wooden stir rod

Step 1. Peel the banana and smash it up in the zip-up plastic bag. Make sure all the lumps are gone.

Step 2. Mix a teaspoon of salt into 1/2 cup of hot water.

Step 3. Pour the salty water into the bag.

Step 4. Seal up the bag and gently mix the saltwater and banana by squeezing the bag. Continue doing this for about 30-40 seconds.

Step 5. Add 1/2 teaspoon of liquid dishwashing soap into the bag. Be careful not to create excess foaming.

Step 6. Secure a coffee filter over a clear glass container or cup, and pour the mix through the filter. This will take some time.

Step 7. Remove the filter. Then, slowly dribble drops of isopropyl alcohol down the side of the cup. You want a layer of alcohol about 1-2 inches (2.5-5 cm) deep. You should see the layer of alcohol form above the rest of the banana juice mix.

Step 8. Wait 8-10 minutes. You should see some bubbles and cloudy material moving around in the alcohol. You can use the wooden stir rod to poke around the cloudy material, and may pick up a little of it on end of the rod.

Take a closer look at the stuff on the stir rod. You are looking at that mysterious substance called DNA! These are the brains of the cell—the blueprints for the design and construction of all living things. Each gram of DNA is capable of storing 215 million gigabytes of information. That's equivalent to the memory of a million laptop computers!

Describe what you see:

_____

_____

_____

_____

_____

Take a moment for prayer. Praise God for His wise genius that provided the wise blueprints for life and the amazing capability of these molecules to store such a huge amount of information!

LIFE APPLICATION

Complete the **Sing** and **Watch** sections of the chapter.

Chapter 3
GOD LOVES REPRODUCTION

PART I

Covers reading material from the beginning of the chapter up to Evolution Is Impossible

VOCABULARY

Match each of the following terms with the correct description.

Sexual reproduction	Two nuclei form within a cell
Interphase	DNA is made out of these
Mitosis	A protective coating forms around a new cell
Cytokinesis	Something makes more of itself, bearing children
Nucleotides	A genetic malady which slows the process of wound clotting and healing
Hemophilia	
Budding	Two identical DNA strands
Sporing	A creature that preys on other creatures
Asexual reproduction	A thin tissue that surrounds a cell or provides separation in a cell
Fibrin	Cell makes a copy of the DNA
Membrane	A clot is sewn together with this kind of cell
Predator	A cell divides into two cells
Sister chromatids	One organism turns into two or more organisms (without the need of a male and female)
	A daughter cell stays connected to the mother cell

COMPREHENSION QUESTIONS

1. How many rabbits could one female and her female children produce in seven years? Why are there a limited number of rabbits in the world?

   _____

   _____

   _____

2. How do we know that God can create a being or a body that can live forever?

   _____

   _____

3. Draw the three phases of cell division below.

Interphase   **Mitosis**   **Cytokinesis**

4. Why is clotting so important to animals out in the wild? Why is it important for us?

   _____

   _____

5. How many processes have to work for clotting to be successful and for animals and humans to survive?

   _____

   _____

6. How does yeast reproduce?

_____

_____

_____

7. Which nucleotides are used in the following codons? These are the most common codons used in the DNA. The first is provided for you. Remember that God's DNA strands are made up of five different nucleotides: adenine (A), thymine (T), guanine (G), cytosine (C), and uracil (U).

AUG—Adenine, Uracil, Guanine

UGG _____

CAG _____

CAC _____

UAC _____

UCC _____

8. How many chromosomes do you get from your father? How many chromosomes do you get from your mother?

_____

_____

9. Why are evolutionists so committed to the idea that God didn't create the DNA, the cell, and life?

_____

_____

10. What are the most intelligent and complicated designs in the universe—produced by God—as explained in this course so far?

_____

_____

_____

FAITH LESSONS

1. Study 2 Corinthians 5:1.

   For we know that if our earthly house, this tent [our body], is destroyed, we have a building from God, a house not made with hands, eternal in the heavens.

   How does this verse compare our body right now to the body we get for eternity (as we believe in Jesus)?

   _____

   _____

   _____

2. What are two things we inherited from Adam, according to Romans 5:12.

   Therefore, just as through one man sin entered the world, and death through sin, and thus death spread to all men, because all sinned. . . (Romans 5:12)

   _____

   _____

3. Read Psalm 94:1-11. What are the wicked saying in verse 7?

   _____

   _____

   Who made the human eye?

   _____

   What does the eye do?

   _____

   _____

   How strong is God's vision? If you can see something going on about 100 yards (80 m) away from you, what can God see?

   _____

   _____

Compare this with Proverbs 15:3. Can God see every robber in the world at the same time?

PART II

Covers reading material from Evolution Is Impossible *to the end of the chapter*

VOCABULARY

Match each of the following terms with the correct description.

Genetics	A section of a chromosome containing certain instructions for one feature of the creature
Chromosome	A certain characteristic of a plant or animal
Gene	A change in the DNA
Codon	Thread-like structures containing DNA
Pistil	An allele that wins out when matched with a recessive allele
Trait	A mutation that hurts the body by preventing the production of skin pigment
Allele	The study of inherited characteristics
Dominant	A protein in red blood cells that delivers oxygen throughout the body
Recessive	The philosophy that man could improve his genetics by eliminating certain people groups with certain genetically-inherited problems.
Mutation	The part of a plant that holds the female egg
Albinism	A genetic possibility inherited from a parent plant or animal
Hemoglobin	An exact copy of another creature
Eugenics	DNA instructions in the form of a three-letter word
Clone	An allele that loses when matched with a dominant allele

COMPREHENSION QUESTIONS

1. What happened when Mendel bred a tall plant with a short plant? Did he get a medium sized plant? What happened with the second generation of the pea plants when they interbred?

_____

_____

_____

2. What part of God's nature is reflected in God's order and variety in creation?

_____

_____

_____

3. How does the evolutionary theory of things evolving into something better differ from reality? How does this theory differ from the Bible?

_____

_____

_____

4. Are mutations helpful or hurtful to humans? List some diseases that come from mutations.

_____

_____

_____

5. What happens to children who are born with genetic problems? What percentage of babies are born with genetic diseases?

_____

_____

_____

6. How do we fix the problem of dying early for people with genetic problems, cancer, heart disease, and other issues? What is the ultimate solution? How can we help children who have genetic problems?

_____

_____

_____

_____

FAITH LESSONS

1. Study Ecclesiastes 8:13 and Proverbs 1:29-33. What happens to scientists and others who do not fear God?

_____

_____

_____

_____

2. Read over 2 Samuel 9 and John 9:1-12. How did David treat this man who was lame in both feet? How did Jesus display his compassion in John 9? What does this teach us concerning our treatment of people who have handicaps?

_____

_____

_____

_____

_____

HANDS-ON SCIENCE

Punnet Squares

The Punnet squares help us to predict what the children of parent plants will look like. If the parents contribute certain genes to the children, will the child look like the mother? Or will the child look like the father? The Punnet square shows all the possible combinations of genes that come from the parents for a certain trait.

Let us take the example of the pea plants that produce child plants both tall and short.

In this case, we will assume that the tall gene is dominant. Because the gene is dominant, we will use the capital letter "T" for the tall allele. The short gene is recessive. So for the short allele we will use the lowercase letter "s."

First Example

First, take the example of a mom plant with a TT gene (two tall alleles). And the dad plant has a ss gene (two short alleles). In this case, we say that the mom plant is purebred for the size trait. And the dad plant is purebred for the size trait.

Dad's gene is "ss." We place the two lowercase s's on the top row.

Mom's gene is "TT." We place two T's on the left column.

The seed for the child plant will get one allele from the mother and one from the father. We fill in the four squares by taking one letter from the left and one letter from above to make a gene for the height trait.

	s	s
T	Ts	Ts
T	Ts	Ts

In this case, 100% of the child plants will be tall, because the tall plant is dominant. Every time the tall allele and the short allele are put together, this will produce a tall plant. So every "Ts" gene in the new plant will produce a tall plant. This means that four out of four child plants will be tall.

This was similar to Gregor Mendel's first generation plants.

	T	S
T	TT	Ts
S	Ts	SS

Second Example

Now, take the example of a mom plant with a "Ts" gene, and a dad plant with a "Ts" gene. Both dad and mom plants are tall, but they have a hidden short trait in the gene. In this case we say that both the dad and the mom plant are hybrid for the size trait.

This was similar to Gregor Mendel's second-generation experiment.

In this case, 3 out of 4 (or 75%) of the plants will be tall. The "TT" and the two "Ts" plants will be tall. Only the "ss" plant will be short.

Third Example

	S	S
S	SS	SS
S	SS	SS

Now, take the example of a mom plant with a "ss" gene, and a dad plant with an "ss" gene. In this case, we say that both the dad and mom are purebred for the size trait.

In this example, 4 out of 4 of the child plants will be short. These parent plants cannot produce tall plants because both parents are purebred for the short trait. Even the children will continue to produce short plants in the next generation if they crossbreed with each other.

Now, fill in the following two Punnett squares.

	T	T
S		
S		

In this case, the dad plant contributes a "TT" gene. And, the mom plant contributes an "ss" gene.

How many of the four child plants will be Tall? _____

How many of the four child plants will be short? _____

In the following case, the dad plant contributes a "Ts" gene. And the mom plant contributes a "TT" gene.

	T	s
T		
T		

How many of the four child plants will be Tall? _____

How many of the four child plants will be short? _____

LIFE APPLICATION

Complete the **Sing** and **Watch** sections of the chapter.

Chapter 4

GOD MADE MICROSCOPIC ORGANISMS

PART I

Covers reading material from the beginning of the chapter up to The Dirtiest Places in the House

Match each of the following terms with the correct description.

Microbiology	Algae, amoebas—organisms that reproduce by mitosis
Microbes	A virus that can stay latent in the body
Fungi	The study of microscopic life forms
Protists	A bacterium resistant to antibiotics
Eubacteria	Non-cellular germs with DNA, but without cell membranes or organelles
Germ	Very dangerous bacteria
Chickenpox	A kingdom of organisms made of eukaryotic cells (without nuclei)
Rhinovirus	Molds, yeasts, mushrooms (spore-producing organisms)
Antibodies	Prevents bad bacteria from reproducing by stopping cell walls from forming
Staphylococcus	
Bubonic plague	Any microbe that can make one sick
Antibiotic	Measures the contagiousness of a disease
Superbug	The most common virus in the world
Reproduction Number	A bacterium spread by rats and squirrels
Viruses	Microscopic organisms
	The body creates these to destroy viruses that attack the body

COMPREHENSION QUESTIONS

1. How many little creatures are crawling around the room right now?

_____

_____

2. What are the uses for all of these microbes?

_____

_____

_____

_____

3. What are the eight kingdoms (if we are applying a biblical view of the world)? Which of the two kingdoms are usually left out by non-Christian biologists?

_____   _____

_____   _____

_____   _____

_____   _____

4. Fill in the blanks in the table below to complete the classifications for the beagle, the cow, and the sparrow. Use the following key and the sample table in the text:

Kingdom Animalia—Animal

Phylum Chordata—Bony spine

Class Mammalia—Mammals (nurses young)

Class Aves—Feathered, egg-laying birds

Order Carnivora—Eats meat

Order Artiodactyla—Even-toed and hoofed

	Beagle	Cow	Sussex Chicken
Kingdom			
Phylum			
Class			
Order			Galliformes
Family		Bovidae	Phasianidae
Genus	Canis	Bos	Gallus
Species	C. lupis	Bos taurus	Sussex

5. Why is a virus not considered a microbe by biologists?

_____

_____

6. What is the most deadly disease caused by microbes, killing the most people each year?

_____

What are the two most common diseases caused by microbes?

_____

_____

7. Where does the common cold get its start in the body? Why?

_____

_____

8. List at least two things white blood cells do to defend the body from germs.

_____

_____

9. How do the antibodies stop the virus from reproducing?

_____

_____

10. Why did cowpox make a good vaccine for smallpox?

_____

_____

11. Why is it risky to eat certain animals, and why should we stay away from sick animals in the wild?

_____

_____

_____

12. How many bacterial cells could develop in 10 hours? What keeps bacteria from taking over the whole world?

_____

_____

13. What is the most deadly bacteria in the world at present? Where is it appearing?

_____

FAITH LESSONS

1. Study Genesis 1:27-28. Suppose that lions and bears were threatening our families and sometimes attacking our brothers and sisters. What should we do about this? If God wants us to rule over the creation, what should we do about bacteria and viruses that attack our bodies and make us sick?

_____

_____

_____

_____

2. Read over these verses from Deuteronomy 14:

"You shall not eat any detestable thing. . . these you shall not eat: the eagle, the vulture, the buzzard. . . You shall not eat anything that dies of itself."

While these requirements had ceremonial elements to them in the Old Testament, do you see any wisdom relating to health in theses verses?

_____

_____

PART II

Covers reading material from The Dirtiest Places in the House *to the end of the chapter*

VOCABULARY

Match each of the following terms with the correct description.

White blood cells	Protein soldiers keep virus-infected cells from multiplying
Interferons	Bacteria found in food poisoning
Probiotics	This protozoan uses a flagellum tail to get around
Salmonella	Protista found in ponds and lakes
Quarantine	Well-known protozoan
Intravenous fluids	Skin disease caused by a fungus
Algae	The long thread-like filaments belonging to a fungus
Protozoa	Fire cytotoxic bullets at cells infected by viruses
Amoeba	When organisms help one another
Euglena	The first antibiotic discovered by Alexander Fleming
Parasites	Separating sick people from others to prevent the spread of disease
Symbiosis	The stems that connect colonies of fungi
Hyphae	Yogurt or buttermilk
Stolons	These, such as the Entamoeba histolytica, can live in people's stomachs
Penicillin	A fungus that attacks wheat
Ringworm	Hurtful protozoa that live off a host, thereby harming it
Black stem rust	Hospitals use this to keep patients from dehydrating

COMPREHENSION QUESTIONS

1. What are the five dirtiest places in the house where microbes are plentiful?

_____

_____

_____

_____

_____

2. What are the three most common forms of bacteria found in poisoned food?

_____

_____

_____

3. What was the most lethal bacteria in recent history, killing 33 people? What was the contaminated fruit?

_____

_____

4. How long can a string of algae grow to be?

_____

5. How do algae consume food?

_____

_____

_____

6. How do the following organisms move around?

Amoeba

_____

Paramecium

_____

_____

Euglena

_____

_____

7. What is the most deadly Protista in the world? How many people does it kill each year?

_____

_____

8. How does the termite consume wood fiber?

_____

_____

_____

9. What is the best way to save lives in Africa, in terms of parasitic diseases?

_____

_____

_____

10. What is the largest living thing in the world?

_____

11. What are three diseases found on the body caused by fungus?

_____

_____

_____

FAITH LESSONS

1. Review the story of the centurion in Matthew 8:5-13.

    If the servant had been afflicted by parasites, what would have to happen with the parasites for the man to be healed?

    _____

    _____

    If the servant had a spinal injury or a brain injury, what would have to happen to his spine or brain for him to be healed?

    _____

    _____

    How does this demonstrate the power of Jesus?

    _____

    _____

    How does this encourage you about your own illnesses, or your death?

    _____

2. Review the story about the poison in the pot in 2 Kings 4:38-41.

    Plant poisons introduce chemicals to the body which can destroy your body tissue. Or it can mess up your body's processes. Also, the Botulinum toxin produced by the bacteria can keep your lung muscles from working. This makes it harder and harder to breathe.

    What did God do to the toxins in the pot to make it edible?

    _____

    _____

    Read Mark 2:17. What is sin compared to in this passage? What does Jesus do for the sin in our souls?

    _____

    _____

    _____

HANDS-ON SCIENCE

The following experiments will take a few days to complete. You should be able to work on both projects at the same time. Both require adult supervision.

1. **Examine spores in mushrooms.**

    Materials You Will Need:

    Fresh mushrooms (from the wild)   Hairspray

    Gloves   Magnifying glass

    Cardboard or construction paper   Disposable cups

    Note: Conduct an internet search for a video entitled "How to Make Mushroom Spore Prints" for a guide in this experiment.

    Procedure

    With adult supervision (either a parent or teacher), identify fresh mushrooms. Be sure to handle mushrooms with gloves. Some can be poisonous. This experiment will be most useful if several different mushrooms are included.

    a. Remove the caps from the mushrooms.

    b. Place the caps on a piece of cardboard or construction paper and label each one.

    c. Place a little drop of water on each of the mushrooms. Cover each mushroom cap with a disposable cup. Wait 24 hours.

    d. Lift the cup and carefully pick up the mushroom straight away from the cardboard.

    e. Allow the spore print to dry over 24 hours, and then spray a layer of hairspray over the print.

    f. Use a magnifying glass to examine the print. How many spores can you see? What does this tell us about God's creation and His commitment to reproduction and life? Record your observations below:

    _____

    _____

    _____

    _____

    _____

2. **How much bacteria is growing in your house?** This experiment identifies the bacteria already crawling around your house. And it will demonstrate how quickly bacteria colonies can grow.

Materials You Will Need

Disposable cupcake liners, and cupcake pan   Sugar

Unflavored powdered gelatin packets   Q-tips

Beef boullion cubes

Procedure

a. Mix 4 cups of cold water, 4 packets of gelatin, 4 beef bouillon cubes, and 4 teaspoons of sugar.

b. With adult supervision, bring the mix to a boil (stirring all the while).

c. Let the mix cool for 5 minutes.

d. With adult supervision, pour contents into cupcake liners in the cupcake pan. The solution should fill up cupcake liners to about 1/3 full.

e. Cover everything and wait until the gelatin is solid.

f. Put each filled cupcake liner into a ziplock bag and refrigerate.

g. Collect samples of bacteria from various places around the house. Take a cotton swab (Q-tip) and swipe various surfaces. Here are some examples. (Be sure to use a new cotton swab each time.)

Sink drain

Toilet bowl

Your mouth

Your armpit

Your palm (before washing with water and after washing with water)

Door handle (Clean the door handle or the sink drain carefully with an antibacterial household cleaner, then take another sample.)

h. Gently wipe the bacteria sample on the Q-tip across a gelatin sample from the refrigerator. Don't break the surface of the gelatin. Be sure to mark each sample with a label, indicating where you got the sample. For example: "Sink Drain," Cleaned Door Handle," "Dirty Door Handle," or "My Mouth."

i. Throw away the Q-tip. Ziplock the plastic bags around each gelatin sample.

j. Store your samples in a dark, warm area.

k. Wait a few days and you should start to see streaks develop over the gelatin. Don't touch these growths. The fuzzy growths are fungi. The streaks are bacterial colonies.

Record your observations and answer the questions below.

_____

_____

_____

_____

_____

_____

Which samples yielded the most microbe growth?

_____

_____

_____

Which samples produced the most diverse colonies?

_____

_____

Did cleaning the surfaces help?

_____

_____

LIFE APPLICATION

Complete the **Sing** and **Watch** sections of the chapter.

Chapter 5

GOD MADE PLANTS

PART I

Covers reading material from the beginning of the chapter up to Flowering Plants

VOCABULARY

Match each of the following terms with the correct description.

Angiosperms	Non-vascular plants growing in highly moist areas
Gymnosperms	The diploid cell when male and female gamete cells come together
Anthophyta,	Seeds delay germination waiting for more ideal conditions
Mosses	Fern leaves
Rhizoids	Sprouting of a seed
Rhizomes	A cell containing DNA chromosomes
Fiddleheads	Seeds that form in flowers, protected by a fruit
Dormancy	A simple sugar used as energy for living organisms
Germination	Green lands rich in vegetation
Gamete	Young ferns
Zygote	Something that happens by chance
Fronds	Flat seeds that form in a cone
Glucose	These use tubes to move nutrients through the plant and are divided into two groups
Adventitious	Root-like structures feeding the mosses
Verdant	Phylum made up of mostly flowering plants
Vascular plants	Fern stems used to pipe water into fronds

COMPREHENSION QUESTIONS

1. If a single apple tree could yield 300 pounds of apples a year, and an apple weighs 1/3 of a pound, how many apples does this tree produce in a year?

   _____

   A 5-acre farm of apples can produce 16,500 bushels of apples in a season. If there are 125 apples in a bushel, how many apples does this farm produce? If apples sell for 33 cents per apple, how much money does the farm earn?

   _____

2. What are the four most commonly grown crops in the world?

   _____

   _____

   _____

   _____

3. How many different kinds of edible fruits, grains, and vegetables are there in the world? Count how many fruits, vegetables, and grains your family eats in a given week.

   _____

   _____

4. How do plants get their food?

   _____

   _____

   _____

5. Besides food, what are the uses for plants?

   _____

   _____

   _____

6. What is the approximate volume of wood in the General Sherman sequoia tree? Round the answer. If the diameter at the bottom is 36 feet, use an average diameter of 18 feet (radius of 9 feet). Here is the calculation:

Volume of wood in the General Sherman sequoia tree = 3.14 x 9 x 9 x 275

_____

_____

If a 2,000 cubic foot house required 1,000 cubic feet of wood, how many homes could be built out of the General Sherman sequoia tree?

_____

7. What are the three kinds of plants?

_____

_____

8. What are at least two differences between a monocot seed and a dicot seed?

_____

_____

9. What did doctors find useful about mosses?

_____

_____

10. In your own words, describe how mosses reproduce.

_____

_____

_____

11. What are the four organs in the seeded vascular plant?

_____

_____

12. In order for seeds to germinate, what are the conditions that have to be just right?

_____

_____

13. How are the "gamete" and the "zygote" related in forming the seed?

_____

_____

_____

FAITH LESSONS

1. Review the story of Jesus feeding the 5,000 (Matthew 14:13-21). How long does it take to grow 12,000 pounds (5,450 kg) of apples on one apple tree? How long do you think it took Jesus to make about 12,000 pounds of food for the 5,000? Which is more impressive?

_____

_____

_____

_____

2. Consider Psalm 104:10-16. What are the works of God mentioned here? What does God do to provide man with food and drink? What does man do to provide this food?

_____

_____

_____

_____

PART II

Covers reading material from Flowering Plants *to the end of the chapter*

VOCABULARY

Match each of the following terms with the correct description.

Sepals	The very center of the flower containing the female gamete
Petal	Tiny pores on the inside of leaves taking in carbon dioxide
Stamen	A green chemical inside the plant leaves
Pistil	Plants designed to store up water for long periods of drought
Ovary	Seeds grow inside of this part of the flowering plant
Cotyledon	These plants bloom and die in the same year
Fruit	These pathways carry water and minerals from the roots to the rest of the plant
Stomata	The colorful parts of the flower
Photosynthesis	These plants flower and produce seeds in the second year
Chlorophyll	These trees lose their leaves during fall and winter months
Carnivorous plants	Trees lose water through needles and leaves
Perennial	Food for the seed is contained in this
Biennial	Distributes food to plant roots
Annual	The process used to turn carbon dioxide and water into plant food
Succulents	Leaf-like structures near the bottom of the flower
Deciduous trees	Plants that eat bugs and turn them into fertilizer
Phloem	Roots that grow out of the side of a tree (in the air)
Xylem	Mature ovary still containing the seeds
Transpiration	Rootstock for these plants come back year after year
Aerial roots	Contains pollen (the male cell)

COMPREHENSION QUESTIONS

1. What is the role of the bee in creating a seed and helping plants to reproduce?

_____

_____

_____

2. In your own words, describe how a seed is made, and how fruit appears from a flower.

_____

_____

_____

3. How does a potato reproduce?

_____

_____

_____

4. Where does all the mass of a tree come from? Why doesn't a towering tree create a huge crater in the dirt?

_____

_____

_____

5. In your own words, describe photosynthesis.

_____

_____

_____

_____

6. Where does the oxygen we breathe come from?

_____

_____

7. List three amazing things about the cobra plant.

_____

_____

8. What is the most dangerous tree in the world? What is the most poisonous plant seed?

_____

_____

9. How did God make cacti to survive in areas like the Atacama desert? Note the Atacama desert in Chile gets 0.1 to 0.6 inches of rain per year (1 mm-15 mm).

_____

_____

10. Provide examples of the following:

Deciduous tree

_____

Evergreen tree

_____

Ginko tree

_____

11. Continue the pattern of addition in the Fibonacci set:

0

1

$0 + 1 = 1$

$1 + 1 = 2$

$1 + 2 = 3$

$2 + 3 = 5$

$3 + 5 = 8$

$5 + 8 = 13$

_____ + _____ = _____

_____ + _____ = _____

_____ + _____ = _____

12. In what parts of nature did our Creator decide to use the Fibonacci pattern?

_____

_____

_____

13. What is the difference between a fruit and a vegetable?

_____

_____

14. What is the most common food for man and animal in the world?

_____

_____

FAITH LESSONS

1. Study the treatment of temptation found in Proverbs 5:1-14. Compare this to the cobra plant. What happens to the person who is taken by temptation in Proverbs 5? What is it that attracts the insect to the cobra plant? What is it that attracts the victim to the temptress in Proverbs 5? What advice do you receive from this passage?

_____

_____

_____

_____

2. Consider Isaiah 65:17-22. How long do trees live? What does this passage teach us about longevity in the kingdom of God? How do you think an eternal lifespan will come about?

_____

_____

_____

HANDS-ON SCIENCE

Complete the following observational experiments.

1. Study the parts of a flowering plant.

   a. Obtain a flowering plant.

   b. Carefully separate the parts of the flower and identify the following parts:

   Stamen (both Anther and Filament)

   Pistil (Ovary, Style, and Stigma)

   Petal

   Sepal

2. Watch seeds germinate on a wet paper towel.

Materials needed:

Paper towel

A few seeds

Procedure

a. Dissect one seed and identify the parts of it.

b. Moisten a paper towel and place a few seeds on the towel.

c. Place it in a sandwich ziplock bag.

d. Place the bag in a darker area of the room (away from direct sunlight).

e. Watch the seeds sprouting over a period of five to seven days. You may wish to transplant your seeds into a garden.

Is the seed a dicot or a monocot? _____

Record progress by day below:

Day 1

_____

Day 2

_____

Day 3

_____

Day 4

_____

Day 5

_____

BEAN SEED
(dicot)

Epicotyl

Hypocotyl

Radicle

Embryo

Seed coat

Cotyledon

LIFE APPLICATION

Complete the **Pray**, **Sing**, and **Watch** sections of the chapter.

Chapter 6

GOD MADE FOOD

VOCABULARY

Match each of the following terms with the correct description.

Scurvy

Beriberi

Vitamins

Metabolism

Carcinogens

Obesity

Weed

Organic food

Crop rotation

Minerals

Morphine

A carbon-based substance in food which prevents certain diseases

Non-carbon-based chemicals God puts in food to keep you healthy

A pain killer taken from the opium plant that is used in hospitals

Changing the type of plant grown in a particular field year to year

Food grown using more manure and compost mixtures rather than man-made fertilizers

A disease common with sailors who lacked citrus in their diet

All the chemical reactions keeping the body alive and turning food into energy

Unwanted plant

Chemicals or foods causing cancers

Extreme extra weight

A disease resulting from a lack of vitamin B1

COMPREHENSION QUESTIONS

1. What was causing sailors to get scurvy?

_____

_____

2. What was causing people in Asian countries to get beriberi?

_____

_____

3. Take a look at the chart explaining the functions of all the vitamins and minerals. What would happen to a body lacking the following vitamins and minerals?

Vitamin A

_____

_____

Vitamin C

_____

_____

Vitamin D

_____

_____

Vitamin E

_____

_____

Calcium

_____

_____

Iron

_____

_____

Phosphorous

_____

_____

Zinc

_____

_____

4. How much nutrition contained in vegetables is reduced by the following food processes?

   Drying foods _____

   Cooking vegetables _____

   Cooking vegetables and draining fluids _____

   Freezing vegetables _____

5. What are some of the reasons you may need to limit the amount of processed foods you eat? List two or three reasons.

   _____

   _____

   _____

   _____

6. How much sugar is contained in the following? If you were limited to 8 teaspoons of sugar a day, which of the following four selections could you eat in one day?

   _____

   a. One can of Dr. Pepper® and 1 Cinnabon® Classic Cinnamon Roll _____

   b. One Snicker's® Chocolate Bar, 1 glass of orange juice, and 1 yogurt (6 oz) _____

c. One apple, 4 slices of bread, and 1 yogurt (6 oz) _____

d. One piece of chocolate cake, 1 apple, and 1 yogurt (6 oz) _____

7. How much has Type 2 diabetes increased since 1960? How much has obesity increased among boys and girls since 1975?

_____

_____

8. How many different plants have been used for medicinal value?

_____

9. What percentage of deaths are attributed to overweight issues in the U.S.?

_____

What percentage of deaths are attributed to smoking and tobacco use in the world?

_____

What percentage of deaths are due to auto accidents in the world? Of these three causes of death, which is most dangerous?

_____

10. How much has the problem of drug overdoses increased since 1950 in the U.S.?

_____

11. Based on the following table showing balanced diets for boys and girls, answer the following questions. You may have to use measuring cups in the kitchen to figure this out.

a. How many pieces of toast make up 5 ounces?

_____

b. How many glasses of milk make up 3 cups?

_____

c. How many green beans make up 2 cups of vegetables?

_____

d. How many hamburgers would you have to eat to make up your requirement for protein in a day? A hamburger (quarter pounder) has 0.7 ounces (18 gm) of protein.

_____

How many chicken breasts would you have to eat to make up your requirement for protein in a day? A chicken breast contains 1.5 ounces (43 gm) of protein.

_____

How many eggs would you have to eat to make up your requirement for protein in a day? An egg has 0.2 ounces (6 gm) of protein.

_____

How many cups of cottage cheese would you have to eat to make up your requirement for protein in a day? A cup of cottage cheese contains 1 ounce (25 gm) of protein.

_____

A Good Balanced Diet—Guidelines for Daily Food Intake

	Girls	_Boys_
Proteins	4-6 ounces	5-6.5 ounces
Fruits (Carbs)	1.5-2 cups	1.5-2 cups
Vegetables (Carbs)	1.5-3 cups	2-3.5 cups
Grains (Carbs)	5-7 ounces	5-9 ounces
Dairy (Fats/Proteins)	3 cups	3 cups

12. How much U.S. land is farmed? How much Mexican land is farmed?

_____

_____

_____

13. What are some of the most common pests that ruin crops around the world? Name at least three.

_____

_____

_____

14. What official requirements must be followed in order to be able to label produce as organic?

_____

_____

_____

15. What are the five ways to take good care of the soil?

_____

_____

_____

_____

_____

FAITH LESSONS

1. Consider 1 Corinthians 6:12-13 once more:

All things are lawful for me, but all things are not helpful. All things are lawful for me, but I will not be brought under the power of any. Foods for the stomach and the stomach for foods. . .

What does it mean to come under the power of a food or drink? What are foods or drinks that might be included in this category?

_____

_____

_____

2. Read over Romans 14:6 and Romans 14:23 once more. What are the two most important principles that should govern our eating? Why should we be careful about judging others about their diets?

_____

_____

_____

HANDS-ON SCIENCE

1. What is your basal metabolic rate? Use an online calculator to figure it out. How does this compare to your average daily diet?

   Research question: How much does your metabolic rate increase if you increase your level of physical activity?

   _____

   _____

   _____

   _____

2. Experiment with your metabolism. Before exercising or doing physical work, vary your food and drink intake. Here are several examples you might try. Choose at least four. Check with your parents/teacher as you organize this experiment. Be sure that you do the same amount of physical exercise when testing each condition. Also, when comparing foods, try to use the same calorie intake for each condition.

   A—Eat a meal/snack of non-sugary carbohydrates.

   B—Eat a meal/snack of sugary carbohydrates.

   C— Eat a meal/snack of mostly protein foods.

   D—Drink a glass of a sugary drink.

   E—Drink a glass of water.

   F—Drink half a glass of water.

   G—Don't eat or drink anything.

   Were you more or less thirsty after exerting yourself physically?

   _____

   _____

   Were you more or less hungry after exerting yourself physically?

   _____

   _____

3. Examine the "Nutrition Facts" labels on some of the processed foods and packaged foods your family eats day to day.

Fill out the following tables.

a. What percentage of your vitamin and mineral requirement are you getting from each serving?

Packaged Food A	Vitamin or Mineral	Percent of Daily Requirement
Description		

Packaged Food B	Vitamin or Mineral	Percent of Daily Requirement
Description		

Packaged Food C	Vitamin or Mineral	Percent of Daily Requirement
Description		

b. How much sugar and salt are contained in each product serving as a percent of the daily recommended value?

_____

How much protein is contained in each product serving?

_____

How many carbohydrates and how much fat are contained in each product serving as a percent of the daily recommended value?

Packaged Food A	Sugar (% of Daily Recommendation)	Salt (% of Daily Recommendation)	Protein (Grams or Ounces)	Carbohydrates (% of Daily Recommendation)	Fats (% of Daily Recommendation)
Description					

Packaged Food B	Sugar (% of Daily Recommendation)	Salt (% of Daily Recommendation)	Protein (Grams or Ounces)	Carbohydrates (% of Daily Recommendation)	Fats (% of Daily Recommendation)
Description					

Packaged Food C	Sugar (% of Daily Recommendation)	Salt (% of Daily Recommendation)	Protein (Grams or Ounces)	Carbohydrates (% of Daily Recommendation)	Fats (% of Daily Recommendation)
Description					

LIFE APPLICATION

Complete the **Pray**, **Sing**, and **Watch** sections of the chapter.

Chapter 7
GOD MADE ANIMALS

PART I

Covers reading material from the beginning of the chapter up to The Wonderful Sense of Hearing

VOCABULARY

Match each of the following terms with the correct description.

Animate creation	Crustaceans like lobsters and shrimp
Ganglia	A flatworm
Vertebrates	Many eyes with the capability of looking in different directions
Sponges	Communicates visual messages to the brain
Decapods	The retina is made up of many of these light-sensitive cells
Myriapods	Creatures with backbones
Compound eyes	The back of the eye
Planarian	The part of God's creation that lives and moves
Mantis shrimp	Extinct creature with amazing eyesight
Trilobite	Centipedes and millipedes
Photoreceptors	Bundles of nerves
Retina	The part of the brain that serves eyesight
Optic nerve	Has remarkable eyesight that picks up 12 different wavelengths
Occipital lobe	
	These creatures can't move but they can pump water

COMPREHENSION QUESTIONS

1. 1. Organize the following creatures according to kingdoms from highest order to lowest order. Name the kingdom if you can.

   An archangel, an amoeba, a beagle, a mosquito, a man

   _____

   _____

2. Why is it impossible to believe that fish turned into birds by evolutionary processes? What is the most important reason we cannot believe this?

   _____

   _____

   _____

3. List at least three categories of animals that do not breathe in oxygen through the lungs.

   _____

   _____

   _____

4. How do fish, sharks, and rays differ from other vertebrates?

   _____

   _____

5. Provide several examples of an exoskeleton.

   _____

   _____

6. What do plant cells look like under a microscope?

   _____

7. What is so impressive about invertebrates (compared to plants)?

_____

_____

8. How does the jellyfish move?

_____

_____

9. How does a clam move in the sand?

_____

_____

10. List at least three amazing features God designed into the dragonfly to enable it to fly.

_____

_____

11. What are two or three benefits of sight?

_____

_____

_____

12. How does the trilobite's eyesight defy evolution?

_____

_____

13. Order the following steps in the right sequence (from 1 to 5) to explain the process of sight.

_____ The lens focuses the light rays on to the retina at the back of the eye.

_____ Many light rays will bounce off the things the eye is looking at.

_____ The photoreceptors on the retina collect the data which will be transmitted to the brain (or the ganglia in some invertebrates).

_____ The light passes through a lens in the front of the eye.

_____ Light rays enter the eye.

FAITH LESSONS

1. Study Matthew 10:29-31 below. Answer the questions. These may require your own research.

   "Are not two sparrows sold for a copper coin? And not one of them falls to the ground apart from your Father's will. But the very hairs of your head are all numbered. Do not fear therefore; you are of more value than many sparrows." (Matthew 10:29-31)

   How many birds are there in the world (estimated)?

   _____

   How many hairs are there on your head (estimated)?

   _____

   How many hairs are there on 7 billion people's heads?

   _____

   What does this teach us about God's care for you and for the rest of His creation?

   _____

   _____

2. List just a few examples of the wonderful wisdom of God in the animal creation—focusing on movement and senses. Then, read Job 42:1-6.

   _____

   _____

   _____

   Then Job answered the Lᴏʀᴅ and said:
   "I know that You can do everything,
   And that no purpose of Yours can be withheld from You.
   You asked, 'Who is this who hides counsel without knowledge?'
   Therefore I have uttered what I did not understand,
   Things too wonderful for me, which I did not know.
   Listen, please, and let me speak;
   You said, 'I will question you, and you shall answer Me.'
   I have heard of You by the hearing of the ear,
   But now my eye sees You.
   Therefore I abhor myself,
   And repent in dust and ashes." (Job 42:1-6)

How do you relate to Job's testimony here?

_____

_____

PART II

Covers reading material from The Wonderful Sense of Hearing *to the end of the chapter*

VOCABULARY

Match each of the following terms with the correct description.

Eardrum	A small bone transmitting sound, located in the middle ear
Hammer	A measurement of the highness or lowness of sound
Cochlea	Animal behavior or display meant to fool or startle other animals
Semicircular canals	Animal with a very complicated defense mechanism, using an explosive technique
Frequency	Animals that transfer a disease from one organism to another
Olfactory system	A tube connecting to the mouth meant to transfer food, sometimes called the throat
Deimatic behavior	
Bombardier beetle	A muscular organ found in insects (and birds) meant to grind up food
Pharynx	A spiral cavity in the inner ear which transfers sound through neural pathways
Esophagus	An organism that lives off of other animals or humans
Gizzard	Reproduction from an egg or ovum without fertilization
Hemolymph	A membrane in the middle ear which vibrates to sound
Excretory tubules	Aquatic animals which eat their food from the bottom of lakes or oceans
Parthenogenesis	A muscular tube meant to transfer food into the stomach
Parasite	Fluid-filled channels in the ear to help the body stay balanced (even in the dark)
Vectors	Waste products from grasshoppers pass through these to the intestines
Bottom feeders	Blood-like fluid found in most invertebrates
	God's design for smelling

COMPREHENSION QUESTIONS

1. How does each of these parts function in the hearing process?

a. Eardrum

_____

_____

b. Hammer

_____

_____

c. Stirrup

_____

_____

d. Cochlea

_____

_____

e. Neurotransmitters

_____

_____

2. Why do you feel dizzy after riding a merry-go-round?

_____

_____

_____

3. What animal has the best hearing?

_____

4. What animals can hear super high frequency noises?

_____

5. What animal can hear super low frequency noises?

_____

6. What has God given the snake to sense its surroundings since this animal is without ears?

_____

7. Why are dogs so much better at smelling than humans?

_____

_____

8. Compare the intelligence of a jellyfish to a plant, a roundworm to a jellyfish, a dog to a roundworm, and a human to a dog.

_____

_____

_____

9. What is the smartest invertebrate? What makes it so smart?

_____

_____

_____

10. What's so amazing about a planarian's reproductive system?

_____

_____

_____

_____

11. How do most invertebrates reproduce?

_____

_____

_____

12. What are the most risky or dangerous animals to eat?

_____

_____

_____

FAITH LESSONS

1. Consider Proverbs 20:12:

The hearing ear and the seeing eye,
The Lord has made them both. (Proverbs 20:12)

What makes these designs so awesome?

_____

_____

_____

How are man's inventions less impressive than these?

_____

_____

_____

2. Compare Acts 10:13, 15 with Acts 15:29.

What does the Lord allow us to eat, according to Acts 10:13, 15?

_____

_____

What did the Apostles consider to be God's law relating to food in Acts 15:29?

_____

_____

_____

Why did God's law regulate this part of our eating?

_____

_____

_____

HANDS-ON SCIENCE

Conduct one of the following observational experiments with adult supervision.

1. Watch a butterfly, moth, or frog go through metamorphosis, changing from a caterpillar or a tadpole into a full-grown creature. Or you might monitor a ladybug. If you watch an insect, record how many days it takes for it to emerge from its pupa.

_____

_____

_____

_____

_____

2. Study the ant. You could purchase an ant farm, or just keep a few ants in a jar, with some small holes pierced through the lid.

Draw a figure of an ant and label its body parts.

Eyes (2)   Thorax

Legs (6)   Abdomen

Head   Antennae (2)

How many segments are in an ant's body?

_____

What does an ant use its feelers for?

_____

What kind of climate does an ant appreciate? Ants will seem a little sluggish at lower temperatures. Experiment by placing them in the refrigerator for about 10 minutes.

_____

Are ants cold-blooded or warm-blooded?

_____

What do ants like to eat? Experiment with things like sugar, lunchmeat, sour lemons, bitter coffee grounds, a piece of strawberry, salt, bread, etc.

_____

Place the food in little cups near the ants. What will the ants go for first?

_____

What does the ant have to teach us, as referenced in Proverbs 6:6-8 and Proverbs 30:24-25? What have you observed about ants that confirms these verses from the Bible?

_____

_____

_____

3. Dissect a grasshopper or cricket using an online video or detailed instructions as your guide. Be sure to give God the glory and the praise for His tremendous wisdom and creativity in making this creature.

LIFE APPLICATION

Complete the **Pray**, **Sing**, and **Watch** sections of the chapter.

Chapter 8
GOD MADE MAN

PART I

Covers reading material from the beginning of the chapter up to The Wonder of the Body's Organs

COMPREHENSION QUESTIONS

1. Order the following from lowest to highest creatures in God's creation. 1 = lowest. 6 = highest.

    _____ Vertebrate animals (with hearts and lungs)

    _____ Microbes

    _____ Vertebrate animals (without hearts and lungs)

    _____ Invertebrate animals

    _____ Humans

    _____ Plants

2. What are the five most common classes of vertebrates? What are two less common classes of vertebrates?

    _____

    _____

    _____

    _____

    _____

    _____

    _____

3. What is one primary difference between vertebrates and invertebrates?

_____

_____

4. What are some of the differences between humans and animals? List at least three differences.

a. _____

b. _____

c. _____

5. Was Neanderthal man an ape, a half-ape/half-man creature, or a man? How did scientists confirm this?

_____

_____

_____

6. Was Lucy an ape, a half-ape/half-man creature, or a man? What are the indications of this?

_____

_____

_____

7. Why is it hard to believe that a fish evolved into an amphibian? Provide several reasons.

_____

_____

_____

8. Compare the moving parts of a car (assembled by humans) and the moving parts in a human body (assembled by God).

_____

_____

_____

9. Name the four types of tissue in the human body and where these tissues are found.

_____

_____

_____

10. How many cells are there in the human body?

_____

How many muscles are there in the human body?

_____

How many different kinds of cells are there in the human body?

_____

How many gallons of blood does the heart pump in 24 hours?

_____

How many white blood cells are there running through your body?

_____

11. What is the difference between a callus and a blister?

_____

_____

12. What are the purposes of skin? Name at least two.

_____

_____

_____

_____

VOCABULARY

Match each of the following terms with the correct description.

Chondrichthyes	Finger-like protrusions in intestines that collect food
Agnatha	Passes on electrical signals to the brain
Red blood cells	Little storage barrels holding insulin
Pancreas	Sharks, rays, and chimeras
Nerve cells	Muscles that work automatically and control the heart
Eukaryotic cells	A muscle that contracts when you want it to
Microvilli	Epidermis forms extra layers over time in a particular area of the hands or feet that are used a lot
Storage granule organelles	Serious form of skin cancer
Epithelial tissue	The tissue that holds the body together
Cardiac muscles	The part of the skin you see
Smooth muscles	The layer of skin just underneath your outer skin
Masseter	Produces insulin to regulate sugar in the body
Connective tissue	The innermost part of the skin
Epidermis	Jawless fish
Dermis	When fluid gets between the dermis and epidermis
Subcutaneous layer	Tissue meant to confine the body and protect the body and its organs
Callus	Involuntary muscles used for the digestive tract, respiratory tract, or urinary tract
Blister	Cells that contain membrane-bound organelles
Melanoma	Carries oxygen around the body
Voluntary muscle	Jaw muscle, the strongest in the body

FAITH LESSONS

1. Read Ezekiel 37:1-10 once more. How does God demonstrate His power in the valley of dry bones? Why is this so awe-inspiring?

_____

_____

_____

2. Psalm 139 tells us that we are "fearfully and wonderfully made." Consider your own body for a few minutes. What is so awesome about your body? List a few things that were not mentioned in the text, if you can.

_____

_____

_____

3. Consider Colossians 3:9-10 and Ephesians 4:23-24. How do you differ from animals? How does an evolutionist try to avoid the very important matter of God's judgment and hell? Why does he do this?

_____

_____

_____

PART II

Covers reading material from The Wonder of the Body's Organs *to the end of the chapter*

VOCABULARY

Match each of the following terms with the correct description.

Cardiovascular system	A hormone used for production of a mother's milk
Respiratory system	Actions initiated by the spinal cord
Endocrine system	A pathway through the neuron
Peripheral nervous system	Concentrated collection of neuron pathways running up the center of the back
Dendrites	
Synapse	Glands regulating body temperature, blood pressure, metabolism, etc.
Axon	Dark spot in eye allows light to enter
Neurotransmitters	Each neuron has 128 of them
Spinal cord	Forms the image using neurons
Reflexes	Heart and blood vessels
Sclera	Controls and focuses light
Cornea	Breathing
Iris	Regulates the size of the pupil
Pupil	Junction between two nerve cells
Retina	Vesicles that carry the signal across the synapses
Prolactin	Ears and eyes
	The white of the eye

COMPREHENSION QUESTIONS

1. Outline the building blocks of the body from smallest to largest.

_____

_____

_____

_____

2. How many organs work together to keep your body going?

_____

_____

3. How much money does the U.S. spend on medical research? How does this compare to the amount of money the U.S. spends on automobile research?

_____

_____

_____

4. Provide two or three examples of how the human eye is more impressive than a camera.

_____

_____

_____

_____

5. How many neurons in your skin can detect surface conditions? How many neurons can sense heat? What would happen if your skin could not detect heat?

_____

_____

_____

6. Give several examples of neurotransmitters.

_____

_____

_____

7. How long does it take for your hand to jerk back from a hot stove (from the moment you touch it)?

_____

_____

8. How sensitive is your hand to feel a scratch in a piece of glass?

_____

_____

9. What are the different kinds of memory? Name at least three to four.

_____

_____

_____

_____

FAITH LESSONS

1. Review Ephesians 4:15-16. How does the human body illustrate the church of Jesus Christ?

_____

_____

_____

_____

2. Why do you think Darwin's thinking on the human eye gave him a "cold shudder"?

_____

_____

_____

_____

3. List a few things that you don't understand, things "too wonderful for you." How does this demonstrate the amazing, infinite wisdom of God?

_____

_____

_____

HANDS-ON SCIENCE

Conduct one of the following observational experiments with adult supervision.

1. Study the efficiency of the endocrine system. Monitor your skin temperature as you move from a cold temperature to a hot temperature, or vice versa. How does your skin temperature adjust to the new environment? Monitor your temperature over a period of about 10-15 minutes. What kind of change do you see?

_____

Minute 1 _____

Minute 2 _____

Minute 3 _____

Minute 4 _____

Minute 5 _____

Minute 6 _____

Minute 7 _____

Minute 8 _____

Minute 9 _____

Minute 10 _____

Minute 11 _____

Minute 12 _____

Minute 13 _____

Minute 14 _____

Minute 15 _____

Observations:

_____

_____

_____

2. Experiment with various kinds of suntan lotion. Choose three different kinds, and lather it on both arms on a hot day. Spend three hours out in the sun doing the same kind of work during the same time of day. Be sure you apply the same amount of each kind for each iteration. Also, be sure that there aren't clouds or other shade that might confound your results. Examine your arms after the test period. Determine a way to measure the area of burn (pink or red areas) on your arms after each test.

Which of the three kinds of suntan lotion was best?

_____

Why should children be concerned about sunburn?

_____

_____

3. Test your reflexes to determine whether your nervous system is working well.

Use a small rubber-tipped hammer (or regular hammer).

Sit on a high stool and let your legs swing freely.

Holding the hammer lightly, gently tap just below your kneecap. You want to gently tap the tendon underneath the bone. Use only one slight tap. It doesn't take much force, and you should do it without causing any pain. It might take a few tries to make it work. If you use a weighted hammer, you can just let gravity do the work at a height of about 4 inches (10-12 cm).

The reflex reaction should happen within about 1 second. You can also use a slow motion smartphone camera to measure the response time. Assess your own response time on both knees. Then, compare that to another person's reflex response time.

_____

Also, take notice if the leg repeatedly responds with a few more kicks. This is called hyperreflexia. No response is called hyporeflexia.

Doctors grade reflexes this way:

0—No response

1—Slight response

2—Normal, quick leg kick (reflex)

3—Very quick leg kick (reflex)

4—Repeating kicks (reflexes)

What grade do you give your reflex response?

_____

What grade would you give your friend's reflex response?

_____

LIFE APPLICATION

Complete the **Pray**, **Sing**, and **Watch** sections of the chapter.

Chapter 9
GOD SUSTAINS HUMAN LIFE

Covers reading material from the beginning of the chapter up to The World's Most Deadly Diseases

COMPREHENSION QUESTIONS

1. What are the three things the body needs to sustain life?

    _____

    _____

    _____

2. What are the things the mouth is designed to do?

    _____

    _____

3. How can you eat and breathe at the same time?

    _____

    _____

4. What are the three contributions the nose provides?

    _____

    _____

5. What did God provide in your throat to prevent food from going down the wrong tube and causing you to choke?

_____

_____

_____

6. What happens to the glottis when you breathe? What is happening to it when you begin to talk or sing?

_____

_____

_____

7. Outline the path followed by the air when you breathe.

_____

_____

_____

_____

_____

8. What are the three things to do when somebody is choking?

_____

_____

_____

9. How do people learn to sing beautifully?

_____

_____

_____

10. How much oxygen is taken out of the air you breathe?

_____

11. How much blood is in the human body?

_____

_____

12. When scientists separate the blood by the centrifuge, what are the three substances they find?

_____

_____

_____

13. Why is it important that the blood carry oxygen around your body? How soon would you die without it?

_____

_____

_____

VOCABULARY

Match each of the following terms with the correct description.

Glottis	Vehicles carrying oxygen to the body
Aspiration	The iron-rich part of the blood that makes it look red
Tracheotomy	Surrounds the glottis; vibrates to makes sounds
Vocal cords	Deoxygenated blood comes back into this section of the heart
Diaphragm muscle	The larynx, where choking occurs
Bronchioles	Exhaling more air than the lungs are inhaling
Hyperventilation	Blood comes back into the heart from the lungs into this section of the heart
Centrifuge	
Antigen	A hole cut by a doctor in the throat to enable a choking victim to breathe
Erythrocytes	The backup node to keep the heart going at a regular pulse
Leukocytes	The main artery leaving the heart
Hemoglobin	The muscle in the body used to breathe
Blood plasma	When water or food makes it into your lungs
Transfusion	The blood vessels carrying oxygenated blood throughout the body
Right atrium	
Left atrium	An instrument used to separate out the different components of the blood
Sinoatrial node	30,000 of these little tubes are in the lungs
Aorta	The part of the heart that keeps the pulse
AV node	The blood vessels returning the deoxygenated blood to the heart
Arteries	Protein coating on red blood cells to stimulate immune response
Veins	Providing replacement blood for a patient who has lost blood
	Hunts and destroys bad germs in the body
	Keeps blood at the right consistency and transports food throughout the body

FAITH LESSONS

1. Study Colossians 1:16-17. Who created all things?

   _____

   How do these things continue to exist?

   _____

   _____

   What are the functions of the human body that must continue to work if the body will live? (List at least three of these functions.)

   _____

   _____

   _____

2. Read Psalm 96:1-3, James 3:1-9, and Psalm 119:172. How does God want us to use our voices?

   _____

   _____

   _____

PART II

Covers reading material from The World's Most Deadly Diseases *to the end of the chapter*

VOCABULARY

Match each of the following terms with the correct description.

Atherosclerosis	A bulge in the wall of the artery
Heart attack	A blockage in the main artery in the brain
Aneurysm	Instrument used to listen for heart murmurs and other problems
Ischemic stroke	Cholesterol and calcium buildup in the arteries
Hemorrhagic stroke	Long tube taking food through the digestive process
Anticoagulants	Measures blood pressure as the heart contracts and is represented by the higher number in the reading
Salivary glands	
Alimentary canal	Organ that filters out unusable stuff from blood and sends it into the bladder as urine
Hydrochloric acid	Low blood pressure reading between heartbeats
Liver	Blood thinner—helps blood to flow
Kidneys	Breaks down proteins
Protease enzyme	Artery develops a leak
Diastolic pressure	When the heart stops due to problems with blood flow or other issues
Systolic pressure	Organ filters dirt and unusable stuff from the blood
Stethoscope	Digestive fluids contain this
	Produces liquid to moisten food as you chew it

COMPREHENSION QUESTIONS

1. What is the most deadly disease in the world? What percentage of deaths occur because of this? What causes this disease?

   _____

   _____

   _____

2. What is the second most deadly disease? What percentage of deaths occur because of this? What causes this?

_____

_____

_____

_____

3. How can you tell if someone has had a stroke? Fill in the words below:

F_____

A_____

S_____

T_____

4. What is the risk of a blood clot in your leg?

_____

5. How much exercise should you get per day (minimum)?

_____

6. If children should limit themselves to 2,300 mg of sodium per day, which of the following would amount to too much sodium in one day? Use the chart on page 274 to help you answer this question.

3 glasses of milk	3 glasses of milk
2 slices of cheese	2 slices of bread
4 slices of bread	1 apple
1 cheeseburger	1 cheeseburger
1 cup of baked beans	1 bag of potato chips

3 glasses of milk

4 slices of bread

1 apple

1 slice of cheese

1 can of beef stew

7. How many teeth does the average child get? How many do adults get?

_____

8. Which animal has the toughest teeth in the world?

_____

9. What happens to the dirt and unusable foods taken into the stomach? Outline the path.

_____

_____

_____

_____

_____

_____

10. How much caffeine would it take to kill you? How many triple shots of coffee would this amount to? How many cherry pits could kill you?

_____

_____

_____

11. What rots out your teeth?

_____

FAITH LESSONS

1. Review Proverbs 4:23. Why is it important for you to take care of your physical heart?

_____

_____

_____

Why is it important for you to know the state of your invisible/spiritual heart? Where is your heart? What is it that you love more than anything else in the world?

_____

_____

_____

2. Consider Matthew 15:16-19 once more. What happens to dirt that comes into the mouth according to the Lord's teaching here?

_____

_____

Does this dirt really defile a man, according to Jesus?

_____

_____

What is it that actually defiles a man?

_____

_____

HANDS-ON SCIENCE

Conduct one of the following observational experiments with adult supervision.

1. Identify your blood type. Here are a few ways to figure it out.

    a. You can narrow down your blood type if you know your parents' blood type.

    O parent x O parent = O child

    O parent x A parent = A or O child

    O parent x B parent = B or O child

    O parent x AB parent = A or B child

    A parent x A parent = A or O child

    A parent x B parent = A, B, AB, or O child

    A parent x AB parent = A, B, or AB child

    B parent x B parent = B or O child

    B parent x AB parent = A, B, or AB child

    AB parent x AB parent = A, B, or AB child

b. You can ask your doctor for your blood type. See if you can identify what your parents' blood type might be from your own.

c. Your parent or teacher could order a blood type test in the mail, and (with adult supervision) you can identify your own blood type.

_____

_____

2. Take your own blood pressure with help from your parent or adult teacher.

_____

3. Take your pulse. At rest, your pulse should be somewhere between 60 and 100 beats per minute.

    The best place to measure the pulse is where an artery is running close to the skin. This includes:

    Your neck   On your temple

    At the back of your knees   On the top of your foot

    Step 1—If you have been active, rest for about five minutes before taking your pulse.

    Step 2—Gently press two fingers on the underside of your wrist.

    Step 3—Once you find the pulse, count the beats for 1 minute. You can also count the beats for 30 seconds, and then multiply your final count by two.

4. Simulate a human lung by building a model using balloons. With adult supervision, view an online video on how to make lungs with balloons.

LIFE APPLICATION

Complete the **Pray**, **Sing**, and **Watch** sections of the chapter.

Chapter 10

GOD RESTORES AND REPRODUCES LIFE

PART I

Covers reading material from the beginning of the chapter up to Implantation

COMPREHENSION QUESTIONS

1. Provide at least two examples of how human technology controls things.

   _____

   _____

   _____

2. List five to six things the body's endocrine system controls.

   _____

   _____

   _____

   _____

3. How are hormones a little bit like the mRNA?

   _____

   _____

   _____

4. How do hormones pass information on to specific cells?

_____

_____

_____

5. What happens on a hot day when your body temperature rises up to 99.4°F (from its normal temperature of 98.6°F)? How does the body respond? Break it down, step by step.

_____

_____

_____

_____

6. Briefly explain what the body does when it detects a new antigen.

_____

_____

_____

7. How do vaccines work?

_____

_____

_____

_____

8. Provide several examples of body parts that can grow back.

_____

_____

_____

9. Put the following steps in order for the development of the human baby in the womb.

_____ The zygote makes its way down the fallopian tubes.

_____ The zygote becomes two cells by mitosis.

_____ The zygote attaches itself to the mother's womb.

_____ The male and female cells join to make a new cell, a new human life.

10. How does every cell determine whether somebody is a boy or a girl?

_____

_____

_____

11. What are three basic biological differences between boys and girls?

_____

_____

_____

_____

VOCABULARY

Match each of the following terms with the correct description.

Endocrine system	High blood sugar
Homeostasis	Female hormone that gets fluids ready to nourish the new baby in the womb
Hypoglycemia	Hormone produced by adrenal gland
Hyperglycemia	Chemical factories that make hormones
Hypothalamus gland	When white blood cells shoot bullets at bad bacteria, fungi, or cancer cells
Epinephrine	Makes white blood cells
Antigen	Chemicals that carry instructions to various parts of the body
Humoral immune response	Controls the body's temperature, minerals, sugar content, water content, etc.
Cell-mediated immunity	The immune response that destroys the invader cells by eating them or by attaching themselves to them
Complement response	Controls the body's temperature
Poliomyelitis	These will eat the invader cells
Autoimmune diseases	When an antibody globs on to the outside of an enemy cell
Thymus gland	When a human baby is only one cell
Phagocytes	Foreign invader stimulating an immune response from the body
Zygote	The hormone that thickens the blood-rich tissue lining the surface of the womb
Zona pellucida	The master gland, producing at least 10 hormones, including your growth hormone
Fimbriae	A virus that used to kill thousands of children
Testosterone	Low blood sugar
Estrogen	The body's immune system attacks normal cells
Progesterone	The right balance for the body
Glands	Male hormone that grows boy-like features in a boy
Pituitary gland	Hair-like things that coax the newly-formed baby up the fallopian tube
Hormones	The outside of the human cell hardens to protect the new baby

FAITH LESSONS

1. Consider Exodus 15:26 below.

   And [the LORD] said, "If you diligently heed the voice of the LORD your God and do what is right in His sight, give ear to His commandments and keep all His statutes, I will put none of the diseases on you which I have brought on the Egyptians. For I am the LORD who heals you."

   What was the ultimate cause of the diseases that came upon the Egyptians?

   _____

   _____

   _____

   What is the source of our healing?

   _____

   _____

   How did God show His mercy to all human beings after man fell into sin?

   _____

   _____

   _____

2. Think about the value of a human being from verses like these: James 3:9, 1 Corinthians 7:14, Psalm 8:4-5. Of how much more value is a human than a dog or cat? Why is the human so valuable?

   _____

   _____

   _____

PART II

Covers reading material from Implantation *to the end of the chapter*

VOCABULARY

Match each of the following terms with the correct description.

Endometrium	Covering of nerve cells in the brain which speeds up the flow of information and learning for the baby
Placenta	
Myelin	Making patients unconscious so they don't feel pain during surgery
Umbilical cord	Scientific word for "womb"
	The center of a bone where red blood cells are made
C-section	
Anesthesia	Skeletal muscles that move when we make the conscious decision to make them move
Bone marrow	Blood-rich layer of tissue lining the mother's womb
Arthritis	Muscles that function without our thinking about it
Voluntary muscles	Ending a baby's life while it is still in the womb
Involuntary muscles	An organ forming inside the mother's womb, which transfers oxygen and food to the baby
Abortion	
Uterus	A surgery where doctors take the baby from the mother's womb
	The breakdown of cartilage causes pain when bone rubs against bone
	Contains tubes connecting the baby's stomach to the placenta

COMPREHENSION QUESTIONS

1. How many months is a human child in the womb before it is born?

_____

2. How is a child nourished for the first 11 weeks in the womb? What is this substance made of?

_____

_____

_____

How is the child nourished for the last 6 months of the pregnancy?

_____

_____

3. What are the three channels in the umbilical cord?

_____

_____

_____

4. Why is it so critical that the placenta not mix the mother's blood with the infant's blood?

_____

_____

_____

5. Draw out the size of the baby for the following weeks in the space provided below:

Weeks 1 and 2

Week 3

Week 4

Week 5

Week 6

Week 7

Week 9

Week 12

Week 16

6. What is the best position for the baby as it is preparing for birth?

_____

_____

7. What were the improvements in medical care that have helped reduce infant mortality?

_____

_____

8. Are bones alive? What are the components of bones?

_____

_____

_____

9. What are the five different kinds of joints in the human body?

_____

_____

_____

_____

10. Identify at least three major differences between the human skeleton and an ape skeleton.

_____

_____

_____

11. How does a bone "heal" itself?

_____

_____

_____

12. Identify at least two major differences between the human's hand dexterity and an ape's hand.

_____

_____

13. How does a gorilla's face differ from a human's face?

_____

_____

14. Give two or three examples of how God has provided the humbler creatures with advanced features.

_____

_____

_____

15. How have people failed to respect the image of God in recent years?

_____

_____

_____

_____

FAITH LESSONS

1. Study Psalm 22:9-10. What was this person doing while in the womb and while nursing? How can we tell that this child had a real personality?

_____

_____

_____

_____

2. Using Psalm 22:9-10, Exodus 20:13, and Exodus 21:22-25, explain why we must take care of the baby in the womb. Why is abortion wrong?

_____

_____

_____

_____

3. Read Philippians 2:5-8. What do we learn from Jesus taking on a human body? Why did He do this?

_____

_____

_____

_____

4. We are fearfully and wonderfully made. From your perspective, what is the most amazing part of the development of the child in the womb?

_____

_____

_____

_____

_____

LIFE APPLICATION

Complete the **Pray**, **Sing**, and **Watch** sections of the chapter.

FINAL EXAM

1. _____ God designed a little motor to run the flagellum.

2. _____ In photosynthesis, the leaves of plants take in oxygen from the air.

3. _____ Mutations like albinism are helpful.

4. _____ Non-vascular plants must grow close to the ground to get water.

5. _____ Wheat is the most commonly grown crop in the world.

6. _____ Obesity is a big contributor to Type 2 Diabetes.

7. _____ The octopus has ganglia instead of a brain.

8. _____ The epidermis is the top layer of skin you can see.

9. _____ It would be dangerous if food passed through your larynx.

10. _____ The world's most deadly disease is Corona virus.

VOCABULARY

Xylem	Used for bringing sugar and nutrition down into the roots of a plant
Phloem	
	Animals with backbones
Parasites	
	Organ in the body producing insulin
Chlorophyll	
	Used for bringing minerals and water up into the plant
Pistil	
	Carries blood filled with carbon dioxide back to the heart
Pancreas	
	Something in the body stirring up the body's immune response
Veins	
Vertebrates	Provides food and oxygen through blood while the baby is in his/her mother's womb
Antigen	
	Keeps leaves green
Placenta	
	Part of plant that contains female gametes
	Hurtful protozoa that live off the host at the expense of the health of the host

SHORT ANSWER

1. Give at least one example of each of the following:

Producers

_____

Consumers

_____

Decomposers

_____

2. Give at least one example of irreducible complexity.

_____

_____

_____

3. Name the four most advanced or complex of God's created material kingdoms.

_____

_____

_____

_____

4. Name one virus-caused disease.

_____

_____

5. Name one bacteria-caused disease.

_____

_____

6. Name two different parts of human blood.

_____

7. How many chromosomes (typically) are found in a human cell from the beginning of life?

_____

_____

ANSWER KEY

CHAPTER 1

VOCABULARY

Confounding	Confusing
Anesthesia	Drugs or gases that will desensitize a person to pain
Extinct	A certain species of animal that died out and there are none left anywhere in the world today
Microbiologist	A scientist who studies tiny creatures
Origins	A study of how the world began or how life began
Experiment	To test a scientific hypothesis or theory
Fossils	The remains or form of an animal cast in rock (usually by water)
Observe	To watch or study God's creation
Hypothesis	A scientific guess that needs to be confirmed by experiments

COMPREHENSION QUESTIONS

1. Science cannot provide truth with total certainty. We can be partially sure of scientific conclusions. We can be totally sure of the truths in God's Word. We can't know for sure what is true by scientific studies. Science cannot answer the question of origins or how this world got here.

2. The moon is not made out of cheese. Men have explored the moon, and they have determined that the moon is made out of rocks and dust—not cheese.

3. Put green leaves into the refrigerator or freezer.

4. The human body can move gracefully, even capable of running, jumping, skating on ice, and twirling around. Whereas rocks cannot move or think, the human mind can think logically, make decisions, design buildings, and invent very complex machines. The human eye can distinguish 10,000,000 shades of colors. Thousands of processes are going on in your body at one time, most of which you are not even thinking about. Cells are reproducing. Wounds are healing themselves. You are breathing. Your blood is taking nutrients and oxygen throughout your body. Your immune system is fighting off disease.

5. a. We must observe.
   b. We must observe cause-and-effect relationships.
   c. You might use instruments like microscopes.
   d. Finally, you would want to repeat your observations over and over again to improve the certainty of your conclusions.
   e. But most importantly, the godly scientist should pray to God for wisdom and insight.

6. Experts can be wrong. They may pretend like they know the answer to your question beyond any doubt. But, experts have been shown to be wrong over and over again.

7. Dates for Discoveries:
   1720—Pastor Cotton Mather of Boston, Massachusetts, discovered the smallpox vaccine.
   1846—Anesthesia was first discovered by several dentists in America.
   1861—A French microbiologist named Louis Pasteur figured out that germs cause bad diseases.
   1895—The X-ray was accidentally discovered by a Christian physicist named Wilhelm Conrad Röntgen.
   1928—The first antibiotic was discovered by Christian researcher Alexander Fleming.
   1970—A Christian inventor named Raymond Damadian

developed Magnetic Resonance Imaging.

8. Charles Darwin and Charles Lyell

9. There wasn't anybody to observe and record every earthquake, flood, and volcanic eruption that had happened over many thousands of years.
Lyell assumed the world was very old.
He assumed the layers of rock around the world had been laid down over a long period of time.
He assumed that Noah's flood never occurred.
He assumed that conditions around the world have always been the same.

10. The radical change, where one kind of animal changes into another kind of animal, has never been observed in a laboratory. Also, Charles Darwin hoped the fossil layer would show lots of varieties of animals developing over time. There was nothing like this to be found in the fossil layers.

11. Scientists would have to observe the mothers giving birth to mutated animals over millions of years in order for the field of evolution to be considered true science.

12. The oldest recorded eyewitness accounts come from a diary of a man writing about 4,000 years ago during the construction of the Great Pyramid of Giza.

13. The death and resurrection of Jesus Christ was the greatest event in history.

14. We know for sure that a worldwide flood came to the earth because God recorded this event in His Word.

FAITH LESSONS

1. God's Word is not tainted by falsehoods. We can be very sure that God's Word is true. We cannot be sure that the hypotheses of evolutionists are true.

2. People refuse to listen to Moses and the prophets because their hearts are hard, and they don't respect God's Word. People would refuse to listen to somebody who rises from the dead because their hearts are hard. They will not be convinced even by a miracle.

3. The Scriptures tell us: "ALL the high hills under the whole heaven were covered. The waters prevailed fifteen cubits upward, and the mountains were covered." (Genesis 7:19-20, emphasis added)
"ALL flesh died that moved on the earth: birds and cattle and beasts and every creeping thing that creeps on the earth, and every man. All in whose nostrils was the breath of the spirit of life, all that was on the dry land, died." (Genesis 7:21-22, emphasis added)

CHAPTER 2, PART I

VOCABULARY

Cell	The most basic, self-contained building block of life
Decomposers	Creatures that live off of dead organisms
Anabolism	Takes useful carbs, fats, and proteins for the body from food
Prokaryotic cell	Cells without organelles
Producers	Organisms like plants that make their own food
Abiogenesis	The idea that life can come from non-life—something like a rock turning into a human being
Organelles	Little organs found in cells
Enzymes	Proteins used to get chemical reactions going in your body
Cytoplasm	The inside of a cell except for the nucleus
Eukaryotic cell	Cells with organelles
Consumers	Creatures that eat plants and animals
Isopropyl alcohol	Rubbing alcohol
Photosynthesis	The method plants use to make their own food
Catabolism	Breaks down fats and carbs for cell energy
Ecosystem	All the living and non-living parts of a community

COMPREHENSION QUESTIONS

1. #1—To glorify God, to love God more, and to praise Him more.
#2—To properly oversee God's creation and to help fight off disease.

2. #1 —Breath of Life
#2—Blood

3. Most Honorable: Angels
Humans
Animals (with blood and breath)
Invertebrates
Plants and Trees
Least Honorable: Rocks

4. Man has the breath of God within him. Adam was created in the image of God in knowledge and righteousness (moral capacity). Animals do not have a sense of morality. Man was also given the responsibility of taking dominion over the creation.

5. Biology: The study of all lifeforms
   Microbiology: The study of micro organisms
   Zoology: The study of animals
   Botany: The study of plants
   Anatomy: The study of the human body and how all the parts fit together
   Physiology: The study of the functions of the parts in the human body

6. Organisms are made of <u>cells</u>.
   Man and animals all experience the sad reality of <u>death</u>.
   Organisms <u>reproduce</u>.
   Organisms need food for <u>energy to exist</u>.
   Cell-based organisms <u>move</u>.
   Organisms start out very small as a single cell or a seed, and they <u>grow</u>.
   Organisms react to outside <u>stimuli</u>.

7. The sun is the most important source of energy, providing food for plants first. Then these plants feed animals and man.

8. Robert Hooke was looking at dead plant cells from old cork wood.

9. Eukaryotic cells

10. Movement
    Reproduction
    Response to external stimuli
    Excretion (or getting rid) of unneeded material
    Provision of nutrition
    Respiration or converting food into useful energy using a chemical reaction
    Growth

FAITH LESSONS

1. God formed man of the dust of the ground and breathed into his nostrils the breath of life.

2. Death came into the world when man sinned against God in the Garden of Eden.

3. The source of life is Jesus Christ.

4. God provides the rain. God provides bread out of the fruitfulness of the earth. He feeds the cattle with grass He grows on the pastures. The energy of the cattle and the donkeys comes from grains grown in the fields.

CHAPTER 2, PART II

VOCABULARY

Organic compounds	Substances made of carbon
Ions	Atoms with more electrons than protons, or more protons than electrons
Metastasis	The condition when cancerous cells are spreading through the body
Larvae	Early stages of insects
Cilia	Finger-like things that can move the cell along
Glucose	The cell's basic food—a kind of carbohydrate
Cancer	A disease that consists of old cells or bad cells in the body reproducing and creating tumors
Irreducible complexity	When lots of things need to work in order for the system to work
Flagellum	A little tail on a cell that helps it move along
Glycogen globules	Your body stores glucose in this form
RNA	Helps build proteins by carrying the blueprint instructions outside of the nucleus to other parts of the cell
Amino acids	The building blocks for proteins
Cytoskeleton	The bones and muscles of a cell
Myosin	A protein that gets things moving in the cell
DNA	The blueprints or instructions for making proteins (and all living things)
Catalyst	Something that triggers a chemical reaction

COMPREHENSION QUESTIONS

1. The yoke of an ostrich egg. You could fit 10,000 human cells on the head of a pin.

2. Houses are mostly made of wood, bricks, and drywall. Our amazing Creator used the raw materials of water, carbohydrates, lipids, proteins, and nucleic acids to make the human cell and the human body. A human body is made up of the following materials:

Water: 60-65%
Fat: 14-20%
Protein: 14-20%
Minerals: 6%
Carbohydrates: 1%

3. Some proteins can make light like little flashlights. Some proteins can detect light. Some can communicate signals, or even detect a signal. Some can function like little motors. They can tie stuff together and untie other things. They can get chemical reactions going. They can check to see if something is right or wrong. They can make hard turtle shells as well as feathers for a bird. Some proteins can combine with other molecules to make complicated machines that replicate DNA, transmit signals to other parts of the cell, and perform other functions.

4. Carbon.

5. The maggots produced an enzyme which slowly digested the dead skin and helped the wounds to heal.

6. The DNA is a double strand, shaped like two worms twisted around each other (in the pattern of a candy cane). The DNA stays inside of the nucleus of the cell. The RNA helps build the protein using the instructions from the DNA. The RNA is a single strand, capable of carrying the information outside of the nucleus into other parts of the cell.

7. There are only 1.4 billion cars in the world, but there are 30,000 times more cells in your body than cars in the world. Cars don't reproduce themselves. You don't find little baby cars squeezing out of the tail pipes of cars. Cars can't repair themselves either.

8. It has a universal joint, bushings, a stator, a rotor, and a driveshaft. Little clamps hold the motor to the cell membrane. The contraption also has a clutch and brakes to slow it down.

9. Birds will continue to live and function—they will not starve to death while their beaks grow larger over time. A cell with only half of a flagellum (or only half of the parts of a flagellum) would not survive.

10. We are pretty sure that smoking and excess radiation cause cancer.

11. Some scientists believe that antioxidants like Vitamin C, Vitamin E, and Beta-carotene can prevent cancer, but there is not much evidence confirming this.
Scientists are pretty much agreed that a healthy immune system can also fight off cancer. It is better if your body is doing the work God has designed it to do.
Finally, some studies have found that supplements can help improve the cell's mitochondrial health.

These include minerals like Magnesium, Phosphate, and Calcium, some co-factors like CoQ10 and NADH, L-Carnitine transporters, and herbs like Curcumin and Schisandrin.

FAITH LESSONS

1. Answers will vary.

2. Step 1—Although they knew God, they did not glorify Him as God
Step 2—Neither were they thankful
Step 3—They became futile in their thoughts, and their foolish hearts were darkened.

CHAPTER 3, PART I

Mitosis	Two nuclei form within a cell
Nucleotides	DNA is made out of these
Sporing	A protective coating forms around a new cell
Sexual reproduction	Something makes more of itself, bearing children
Hemophilia	A genetic malady which slows the process of wound clotting and healing
Sister chromatids	Two identical DNA strands
Predator	A creature that preys on other creatures
Membrane	A thin tissue that surrounds a cell or provides separation in a cell
Interphase	Cell makes a copy of the DNA
Fibrin	A clot is sewn together with this kind of cell
Cytokinesis	A cell divides into two cells
Asexual reproduction	One organism turns into two or more organisms (without the need of a male and female)
Budding	A daughter cell stays connected to the mother cell

COMPREHENSION QUESTIONS

1. 185 billion rabbits. One reason for the limited number of rabbits is that they cannot defend themselves from predators.

2. Jesus is risen from the dead and He will live forever (Revelation 1:18). He has promised that we will live forever if we believe in the only begotten Son of God (John 3:16). Scripture also tells us that God has made an eternal house for us in the heavens that has not been made with hands (2 Corinthians 5:1).

3.

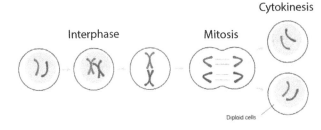

4. Clotting is important for animals in the wild because they do not have access to medical help. Their skin must automatically heal up the cuts and scrapes. Clotting is important for us because it hurries up the healing process for us. And we don't want to have to go to the doctor every time we get a cut.

5. About 40 processes.

6. Yeast will reproduce in a process called budding. After mitosis, the daughter will form a little bump or bud at the yeast's cell wall. Sometimes this will break off, but sometimes it stays attached. Eventually a granddaughter bud will form on the daughter bud, and extended chains of yeast develop.

7. AUG—Adenine, Uracil, Guanine
UGG—Uracil, Guanine, Guanine
CAG—Cytosine, Adenine, Guanine
CAC—Cytosine, Adenine, Cytosine
UAC—Uracil, Adenine, Cytosine
UCC—Uracil, Cytosine, Cytosine

8. Twenty-three from your father, and 23 from your mother.

9. They don't want God. They don't want to be morally responsible to Him. They don't want God to tell them what to do.

10. The most complicated designs God has produced for us include: all of the processes in the cell, the DNA, the RNA, the defense mechanisms, the clotting, the little flagella motors, and the cell reproductive systems.

FAITH LESSONS

1. The body here is only a tent. The body we get in heaven will be a permanent building.

2. We inherited sin and death from Adam.

3. The wicked pretend that God cannot see what they are doing. God made the human eye. The human eye can see things. But God's vision is much better than our vision. He can see everything going on everywhere around the world. Yes. God can see every robber and every sinner in the world at the same time. God is much more aware of what is going on in the world than we are. He gave us sight, but His senses or awareness of reality are much more acute than ours.

CHAPTER 3, PART II

VOCABULARY

Gene	A section of a chromosome containing certain instructions for one feature of the creature
Trait	A certain characteristic of a plant or animal
Mutation	A change in the DNA
Chromosome	Thread-like structures containing DNA
Dominant	An allele that wins out when matched with a recessive allele
Albinism	A mutation that hurts the body by preventing the production of skin pigment
Genetics	The study of inherited characteristics
Hemoglobin	A protein in red blood cells that delivers oxygen throughout the body
Eugenics	The philosophy that man could improve his genetics by eliminating certain people groups with certain genetically-inherited problems.
Pistil	The part of a plant that holds the female egg
Allele	A genetic possibility inherited from a parent plant or animal
Clone	An exact copy of another creature
Codon	DNA instructions in the form of a three-letter word

Recessive	An allele that loses when matched with a dominant allele

COMPREHENSION QUESTIONS

1. Mendel ended up with all tall plants in the first generation. However, three quarters of the plants were tall, while one quarter of the plants were short in the second generation. The Punnett squares example illustrates how this happens.

2. The Trinity. God is unity. He is One God. But, He is also three Persons—the Father, the Son, and the Holy Spirit.

3. Actually, the natural world is not improving and developing higher life forms. The Bible presents the human lifespan as decreasing after the flood. According to God's plans, bad genetic mutations were introduced into the human cells after Adam fell into sin. This might have continued after the flood.

4. Mutations are hurtful. It's estimated that mutations are 1000 times more harmful than they are helpful. In humans, mutations produce diseases like cancer, albinism, hemophilia, cystic fibrosis, and sickle cell anemia.

5. Children born with genetic problems usually die a little earlier than the average person. About 0.25% of babies born have genetic issues.

6. We trust in Jesus who has risen from the dead, and He fixes the problem of death for us. Instead of working on ways to kill babies with these problems, it is always better to find ways to improve their lives on this earth. Thus, the average lifespan of children with Down syndrome has improved from 25 years to 60 years just since 1983. Much of this improvement comes from taking children out of institutions and keeping them in loving homes with their families.

FAITH LESSONS

1. Those who do not fear God will find their lives cut short. They will fear evil, and find themselves in trouble.

2. David brought Mephibosheth to his own table every day, and took good care of the man. Jesus healed the man who was born blind. Answers may vary.

HANDS-ON SCIENCE

	T	T
S	Ts	Ts
S	Ts	Ts

How many of the four child plants will be Tall? 4 (100%)

How many of the four child plants will be short? 0

	S	S
T	Ts	Ts
T	Ts	Ts

How many of the four child plants will be Tall? 4 (100%)

How many of the four child plants will be short? 0

CHAPTER 4, PART I

VOCABULARY

Protists	Algae, amoebas—organisms that reproduce by mitosis
Chickenpox	A virus that can stay latent in the body
Microbiology	The study of microscopic life forms
Superbug	A bacterium resistant to antibiotics
Viruses	Non-cellular germs with DNA, but without cell membranes or organelles

Staphylococcus	Very dangerous bacteria
Eubacteria	A kingdom of organisms made of eukaryotic cells (without nuclei)
Fungi	Molds, yeasts, mushrooms (spore-producing organisms)
Antibiotic	Prevents bad bacteria from reproducing by stopping cell walls from forming
Germ	Any microbe that can make one sick
Reproduction Number	Measures the contagiousness of a disease
Rhinovirus	The most common virus in the world
Bubonic plague	A bacterium spread by rats and squirrels
Microbes	Microscopic organisms
Antibodies	The body creates these to destroy viruses that attack the body

COMPREHENSION QUESTIONS

1. About 37,000,000 creatures are in the room.

2. Some microorganisms are edible for animals. Some microorganisms clean up God's world of manure and other waste products. Others help us to digest our food.

3. Human
   Animals with the breath of life
   Animals without the breath of life
   Plants
   Protista
   Fungi
   Archaebacteria
   Eubacteria
   Non-Christians do not distinguish humans from animals. And, they do not separate out animals with the breath of life from animals without the breath of life.

4.

	Beagle	Cow	Sussex Chicken
Kingdom	Animalia	Animalia	Animalia
Phylum	Chordata	Chordata	Chordata
Class	Mammalia	Mammalia	Aves
Order	Carnivora	Artiodactyla	Galliformes
Family	Canidae	Bovidae	Phasianidae
Genus	Canis	Bos	Gallus
Species	C. lupus	Bos taurus	Sussex

5. A virus is not a microbe because it cannot reproduce. A virus is only DNA without a cell wall or other organelles.

6. Pneumonia kills the most. Common colds and diarrhea are the most common.

7. The rhinovirus usually gets its start in the nose because it spreads when the temperature hovers around 91–95°F (33–35°C).

8. The job of the cytotoxic t-cells (white blood cells) is to patrol the body and identify the bad viruses when they get into the body and penetrate a cell. The t-cells start firing cytotoxic granules at the infected cell like bullets from a gun. One particular cytotoxin called perforin actually makes holes in the cell to introduce enzymes. These enzymes are tasked with destroying the cell and the virus within it.

9. They attach themselves to the virus and make it impossible for the virus to attach itself to another cell, thereby stopping their reproduction.

10. It was a weaker virus that didn't hurt people as much. So this virus helped the body to make antibodies which would go after both the cowpox and the smallpox.

11. Sick animals can convey diseases. The Scriptures also warn about consuming certain animals, particularly carnivores, rodents, cats, monkeys, and bats. Humans can contract viruses that adapt and attach to humans when we consume exotic animals. These unconventional diets can be very risky and bring much suffering to mankind.

12. A bacterium can reproduce in just 20 minutes. At this rate, you would see 500 new cells develop in 3 hours, 32,000 in 5 hours, and 1 billion in 10 hours. In a week, there would be so much bacteria in the world it could fill up the earth. However, there are some limitations to bacterial growth. First, bacteria need food to live, and if they don't have access to food or oxygen, they will die out. If a colony of bacteria is sitting on a food source, the cells in the middle or towards the top of the heap don't have access to the food. It gets too crowded in the colony, and so there comes a point at which the cells die faster than they reproduce. Consequently, the largest bacterial colonies are no bigger than a pea. Also, bacteria are pretty picky when it comes to temperature and pH range. There needs to be a high degree of moisture in the environment for a bacterium to grow.

13. Mycrobacterium tuberculosis is the most deadly bacteria right now, killing about 1.7 million people a year. Over 120 countries have seen instances of this form of tuberculosis (TB), which is most commonly found in Russia, Ukraine, China, Egypt, Peru, and Ecuador.

1. Answers will vary.

2. Answers will vary.

CHAPTER 4, PART II

VOCABULARY

Interferons	Protein soldiers keep virus-infected cells from multiplying
Salmonella	Bacteria found in food poisoning
Euglena	This protozoan uses a flagellum tail to get around
Algae	Protista found in ponds and lakes
Amoeba	Well-known protozoan
Ringworm	Skin disease caused by a fungus
Hyphae	The long thread-like filaments belonging to a fungus
White blood cells	Fire cytotoxic bullets at cells infected by viruses
Symbiosis	When organisms help one another
Penicillin	The first antibiotic discovered by Alexander Fleming
Quarantine	Separating sick people from others to prevent the spread of disease
Stolons	The stems that connect colonies of fungi
Probiotics	Yogurt or buttermilk
Protozoa	These, such as the Entamoeba histolytica, can live in people's stomachs
Black stem rust	A fungus that attacks wheat
Parasites	Hurtful protozoa that live off a host, thereby harming it
Intravenous fluids	Hospitals use this to keep patients from dehydrating

COMPREHENSION QUESTIONS

1. The dirtiest places are:
   The dish sponge in the kitchen sink
   The toothbrush holder in the bathroom
   Pet water or food bowls
   The kitchen sink
   The coffee water reservoir

2. Salmonella, listeria, and E. coli.

3. Listeria contaminated cantaloupe.

4. 330 feet (100 meters) long.

5. They usually produce their food by photosynthesis. Some algae will also consume food in their environments.

6. Amoeba—Pseudopods, a bulging membrane that forms legs
   Paramecium—Cilia
   Euglena—Flagella

7. The plasmodium is the most common and deadly Protista, spread by mosquitoes in Africa and elsewhere around the world. Malaria kills around 500,000 people a year worldwide.

8. Our Creator provided termites with little protozoa called the Trichonympha that help the termite digest cellulose.

9. Having access to clean water. But also:
   — Avoid immoral and sinful behavior.
   — Move outhouses away from where people live. Use flushing toilets where possible. Keep all sewage holes well covered.
   — Make soap widely available. Promote hand washing before preparing food, before eating, and after using the restroom.

10. In Oregon and Washington State, huge underground networks of mushrooms have been discovered, covering about 2,200 acres (890 hectares). That's about two miles by two miles (3.2 km by 3.2 km) of continuous growth of honey mushroom.

11. Ringworm, athlete's foot, and thrush.

FAITH LESSONS

1. Answers will vary.

2. Answers will vary.

CHAPTER 5, PART I

Mosses	Non-vascular plants growing in highly moist areas
Zygote	The diploid cell when male and female gamete cells come together

Dormancy	Seeds delay germination, waiting for more ideal conditions
Fronds	Fern leaves
Germination	Sprouting of a seed
Gamete	A cell containing DNA chromosomes
Angiosperms	Seeds that form in flowers, protected by a fruit
Glucose	A simple sugar used as energy for living organisms
Verdant	Green lands rich in vegetation
Fiddleheads	Young ferns
Adventitious	Something that happens by chance
Gymnosperms	Flat seeds that form in a cone
Vascular plants	These use tubes to move nutrients through the plant and are divided into two groups
Rhizoids	Root-like structures feeding the mosses
Anthophyta	Phylum made up of mostly flowering plants
Rhizomes	Fern stems used to pipe water into fronds

COMPREHENSION QUESTIONS

1. A single tree could produce 900 apples per year. The farm produces 2,062,500 apples, and earns $680,625 per year.

2. Sugarcane, corn, rice, and wheat.

3. 20,000. Answers may vary.

4. Plants make their own food using photosynthesis.

5. Plants are also used for clothing and shelter. Incredibly, the earth produces about one billion tons of wood each year for our homes, furniture, and paper. And 30% of the clothing in the world is made of cotton, wool, and natural fibers.

6. 70,000 cubic feet of wood. That's enough to build 70 homes.

7. There are non-vascular plants, seedless vascular plants, and seeded vascular plants.

8. A monocot is a seed that has only one embryonic leaf or cotyledon. A dicot contains two parts. In addition, monocots are usually flat while dicots are more rounded. When a monocot germinates, it produces a single leaf. When a dicot germinates, it pops out with at least two leaves. Monocot leaves tend to be narrower, and dicot leaves are round or elliptical. Monocot stems are also softer and more fleshy, while dicot stems are stiffer.

9. During World War I, several British doctors found that two kinds of mosses were very good for staunching blood and helping wounds heal: *S. papillosum* and *S. palustre*. They were twice as absorbent as cotton and kept the acidity level high (and the ph level low). High acidity slows down the growth of bad bacteria in the wound.

10. When the spore first sprouts, it produces the protonema, which develops into leafy shoots. Either eggs or male reproductive cells form on the leafy shoots. When water collects on the shoots, the male cells swim around until they find an egg on a female leafy shoot. Thousands of spores are formed when they meet. Next, stalks grow out of the leafy shoots and extend capsules into the air. The Lord made these capsules to collect the spores. When the timing is right, the capsule opens, and the spores are carried away by the wind. Each spore can grow into a new moss plant. By this means, the moss spreads itself like a beautiful carpet of green across the ground.

11. Roots, stems, leaves, and reproductive organs.

12. The Creator made the seed such that it can sense temperature, light, moisture, and nutrients in the soil.

13. One male gamete + One female gamete = One zygote

FAITH LESSONS

1. Answers may vary. It takes about 40 years for an apple tree to yield that many apples. Jesus provided 12,000 pounds of food in a few hours.

2. Answers may vary. God brings rain and snow to water the valleys and fields. God feeds the wild animals. God causes grass to grow for the cattle. God gives man vegetation—things to eat from the earth. Man then makes wine from the fruit of the earth. Man makes bread and oils from olives, etc. God grows trees.

CHAPTER 5, PART II

VOCABULARY

Pistil	The very center of the flower containing the female gamete
Stomata	Tiny pores on the inside of leaves taking in carbon dioxide

Chlorophyll	A green chemical inside the plant leaves
Succulents	Plants designed to store up water for long periods of drought
Ovary	Seeds grow inside of this part of the flowering plant
Annual	These plants bloom and die in the same year
Xylem	These pathways carry water and minerals from the roots to the rest of the plant
Petal	The colorful parts of the flower
Biennial	These plants flower and produce seeds in the second year
Deciduous trees	These trees lose their leaves during fall and winter months
Transpiration	Trees lose water through needles and leaves
Cotyledon	Food for the seed is contained in this
Phloem	Distributes food to plant roots
Photosynthesis	The process used to turn carbon dioxide and water into plant food
Sepals	Leaf-like structures near the bottom of the flower
Carnivorous plants	Plants that eat bugs and turn them into fertilizer
Aerial roots	Roots that grow out of the side of a tree (in the air)
Fruit	Mature ovary still containing the seeds
Perennial	Rootstock for these plants come back year after year
Stamen	Contains pollen (the male cell)

COMPRESSION QUESTIONS

1. A bee crawls around on the anther of a stamen. She gets the sticky pollen all over her feet and wings. As she flits from flower to flower, the bee rubs her feet and wings up against the flower's stigma (at the top of the pistil). The stigma is pretty sticky, so it attracts the pollen carried by the bee.

2. Answers may vary. When the pollen grain (male gamete) lands on the stigma, it makes its way down the pistil by growing a long tube through the style to the ovary. The seeds grow inside the ovary. Once inside the ovary, the pollen's DNA joins up with the DNA of the eggs (female gametes). The eggs develop into seeds. Each seed is

made up of the zygote or embryo, some food, and a shell to protect the little embryo. The food is stored inside the seed in little containers called cotyledons. The blossom will then begin to shrivel, and the ovary expands, closing the seeds inside. All that's left of the flower is the dried-up sepal at the bottom of the fruit. Most importantly, at least for humans and animals, is what happens with the ovary. It turns into edible food, such as an apple or some other fruit.

3. Potatoes are large, fat tubors that grow off an underground stem. If you let them sit around long enough, they will grow little buds called "eyes." If planted in the ground, these will form new plants.

4. The matter collected in a tree doesn't come from the dirt. The tree is mainly made up of carbon. The carbon comes from carbon dioxide, and carbon dioxide comes from the atmosphere.

5. Tiny little pores on the underside of the leaves (called stomata) take in carbon dioxide. Water is carried up to the plant leaves from the soil. A green chemical called chlorophyll is contained in the chloroplasts of plant cells. Chloroplasts absorb energy from the sun. This energy is used to make food by a special chemical reaction. The carbon dioxide and water combine in the reaction to produce sugar (glucose). Oxygen is released from the plant in the form of gas.

6. About 30% of the oxygen we breathe comes from forests and fields, and the other 70% comes from marine plants in the oceans. The amount of oxygen required by each person is equivalent to the oxygen produced by 49 trees. Thankfully, there are 400 billion trees in the world and a lot of marine plants to keep us all well stocked in oxygen!

7. Answers may vary, but should include some of the following: Insects are lured to the leaf's opening by nectar-covered, fang-like appendages. The opening itself is also saturated with nectar, smooth and slippery. Landing on this tempting cover, the unsuspecting insect soon finds itself sliding down the tube. When the bug tries to fly up and out, it gets confused by the many transparent "windows" on the plant's hood. The poor insect then keeps bumping into the hood, missing the opening. Then it will slide down the slippery tube once more. Near the bottom of the tube, the insect runs into a lining of hairs all pointing downward into a pool of digestive juices. Try as it may, the little bug cannot escape by climbing over the hairs. Finally, in exhaustion the victim will collapse into the pool of toxic juices. God has made the cobra plant very complex. On the one hand, the plant makes its own food by photosynthesis. Then it also uses water to produce two more substances—the sweet nectar to attract insects, and the toxic liquid to digest them!

8. The most poisonous tree in the world is the manchineel, which grows in Florida and the Caribbean. Sap from the tree can cause an immediate breakout of blisters. If the sap comes in contact with your eyes, you could go blind immediately. A single bite of the tree's fruit could be fatal. Should someone burn the wood, smoke from the fire could cause blindness. The most dangerous plant seed in the world is the *Abrus precatorius*, also called the rosary pea. It has a tough exterior shell, but if it is scratched and ingested, just 3 micrograms could kill an adult. That's one tenth of one drop of fluid.

9. Succulent stems are designed with ridges to catch water, so as to absorb as much as possible. The spines on the cactus were designed to discourage animals from eating the plant. Nobody really wants a cactus needle stuck in their throat. Also, cactus roots spread out just below the surface of the ground to absorb all the rainwater they can get.

10. Deciduous tree—oak, maple, elm
Evergreen tree—pines, spruces, firs
Ginkgo tree—The maidenhair tree, stangeria, Australian bowenia.

11. The next three iterations of the fibonacci set:
8 + 13 = 21
13 + 21 = 34
21 + 34 = 55

12. Spirals found in seashells, flowers, pineapples, pine cones, fern leaves, tornadoes, and galaxies.

13. Fruit is what forms around a seed. It is part of the reproductive system of a plant. The vegetable is any other edible part of a plant.

14. The most common food is grass and grass seed.

FAITH LESSONS

1. The victim of temptation in Proverbs 5 will see his flesh and body consumed and taken to "total ruin." The insect is attracted to the cobra plant by the sweet nectar. The man is tempted in Proverbs 5 by a mouth "smoother than oil."

2. Trees can live up to 4,500 years. Many trees live hundreds of years. But according to Isaiah 65 we will live longer than trees. This points to the final resurrection—eternal life. This comes about by the resurrection of Jesus Christ and our faith in Him.

CHAPTER 6

VOCABULARY

Vitamins	A carbon-based substance in food which prevents certain diseases
Minerals	Non-carbon-based chemicals God puts in food to keep you healthy
Morphine	A pain killer taken from the opium plant that is used in hospitals
Crop rotation	Changing the type of plant grown in a particular field year to year
Organic food	Food grown using more manure and compost mixtures rather than man-made fertilizers
Scurvy	A disease common with sailors who lacked citrus in their diet
Metabolism	All the chemical reactions keeping the body alive and turning food into energy
Weed	Unwanted plant
Carcinogens	Chemicals or foods causing cancers
Obesity	Extreme extra weight
Beriberi	A disease resulting from a lack of vitamin B1

COMPREHENSION QUESTIONS

1. The sailors weren't getting vitamin C (found in citrus fruits).

2. The people in Asia weren't getting vitamin B1 (found in the whole grain rice).

3. Vitamin A—Vision and growth would become a problem.
Vitamin C—Wounds wouldn't heal well. Immune system problems.
Vitamin D—Blood pressure problems, bone problems, immune system problems.
Vitamin E—Blood vessels problems, and immune system problems.
Calcium—Blood clotting problems, weak bones and teeth.
Iron—Loss of energy, stunted growth, wound healing and immune system problems.
Phosphorous—Loss of energy, bone formation problems for children.
Zinc—Growth problems, immune system problems, taste problems, nervous system problems, reproductive

system problems.

4. Drying foods—50%
Cooking vegetables—25-40%
Cooking vegetables and draining fluids—40-75%
Freezing vegetables—0%

5. Processed food can be highly addictive.
Some additives to processed foods can cause weak bones, kidney problems, obesity, and aging. The high levels of phosphates in soda drinks can weaken your bones and break down internal organs.
Pound for pound, fresh food is usually cheaper than processed food. If a pound of potato chips is priced at $4.00, you could purchase a pound of apples for $1.30, or a pound of potatoes for $0.75.
Some processed foods can cause chronic inflammation, probably due to the use of refined sugars, excess salt, and processed grains.
Junk food can also ruin your digestive system. Remember, the same Creator who made your digestive system also made the food to go into it. Without natural fibers, enzymes, and vitamins, the body will have a hard time processing the substances.
Certain processed foods can also wreak havoc on your mind. People complain of brain fog or difficulty concentrating. Often, this is linked to interruptions in the digestive system.

6. a. One can of Dr. Pepper® and 1 Cinnabon® Classic Cinnamon Roll—16 teaspoons
b. One Snicker's® Chocolate Bar, 1 glass of orange juice, 1 yogurt (6 oz)—7.5 teaspoons
c. One apple, 4 slices of bread, and 1 yogurt (6 oz)—4. 5 teaspoons
d. One piece of chocolate cake, 1 apple, and 1 yogurt (6 oz)—10 teaspoons
If limited to 8 teaspoons of sugar in a day, you could eat b) or c) in one day.

7. Type 2 diabetes has increased by about ten-fold. Obesity has increased by about ten-fold.

8. 35,000-70,000 plants have been used for their medicinal value.

9. About 20% of American deaths are due to overweight issues. About 13% of deaths are due to tobacco use, and 2.4% of deaths are due to auto accidents. Obesity is the most dangerous killer now.

10. Drug overdose rates have increased twenty-fold since 1950.

11. a. Answers may vary a bit. Five pieces of toast.
b. Answers may vary a bit. Three small glasses.
c. Answers may vary a bit. Forty green beans.
d. Answers may vary a bit.

12. The U.S. farms about 18% of the total land mass. Mexico farms about 1% of the total land mass.

13. The most common pests are locusts (grasshoppers), Japanese beetles, aphids, whiteflies, the Colorado potato beetle, stink bugs, the spider mite, the diamondback moth, the red flower beetle, the fall armyworm, and the brown planthopper.

14. Officially, produce can be labeled organic if it has grown in soil in which no man-made fertilizers and pesticides have been added to it for three years.

15. Five ways to take good care of the soil:
a. Keep erosion down. Wind and water can brush away the topsoil, leaving very little room for plants to grow deep roots.
b. Minimize the tillage (turning over the soil).
c. Providing enough water.
d. Keeping enough organic material mixed in (and limiting inorganic material). Animal waste products and dead plant residues are usually good for the soil.
e. Providing mulch for shade and moisture retention. Keeping soil cool.

FAITH LESSONS

1. Answers may vary. To be dependent upon the substance. Alcohol, sweets, tobacco, pop, coffee, etc.

2. Answers may vary. Thanksgiving and faith. We should be careful about judging others about their diet because it's really hard to know the condition of their hearts. We don't know whether they are thankful and full of faith when they eat. Also, the Bible gives a great deal of liberty when it comes to food and drink choices.

CHAPTER 7, PART I

Decapods	Crustaceans like lobsters and shrimp
Planarian	A flatworm
Compound eyes	Many eyes with the capability of looking in different directions
Optic nerve	Communicates visual messages to the brain
Photoreceptors	The retina is made up of many of these light-sensitive cells
Vertebrates	Creatures with backbones
Retina	The back of the eye
Animate creation	The part of God's creation that lives and moves
Trilobite	Extinct creature with amazing eyesight
Myriapods	Centipedes and millipedes
Ganglia	Bundles of nerves
Occipital lobe	The part of the brain that serves eyesight
Mantis shrimp	Has remarkable eyesight that picks up 12 different wavelengths
Sponges	These creatures can't move but they can pump water

COMPREHENSION QUESTIONS

1. An archangel—Angels
    A man—Humans
    A beagle—Animal with the breath of life
    A mosquito—Animal without the breath of life
    An amoeba—Protista

2. There is no evidence of this gradual process. If a fish turns into a bird over a billion years, where are all the half-fish, half-bird creatures in the fossil record? If a worm turns into a fish over a billion years, where are the millions of half-worm, half-fish creatures in the fossil record? God's Word tells us that God created the world in six days. It did not happen over billions of years.

3. Phylum Porifera (sponges)
    Phylum Cnidaria (jellyfish and sea anemones)
    Phylum Echinodermata (sea stars)
    Phylum Platyhelminthes (flatworms and tapeworms)
    Phylum Mollusca (octopi, clams, and squids)
    Phylum Arthropoda (crabs, insects, spiders)
    Part of Phylum Chordate (fish, sharks, and rays)

4. They do not have hearts and lungs.

5. The cricket's crunchy skin and the snail's shell are examples of exoskeletons.

6. They look rectangular.

7. The most impressive features of animals without the breath of life are movement, sensing and response mechanisms, feeding methods, defense mechanisms, and reproduction.

8. The Creator equipped the jellyfish with muscles around its gastrovascular cavity (or stomach) near the opening of the jellyfish's bell. These muscles squeeze down on the cavity, which contains seawater. This propels the jellyfish along in slow, jerky movements.

9. To move through the sand, the clam extends a muscular foot. Then the "toes" of the foot expand into the sand, anchoring it. The foot muscle contracts, pulling its body forward an inch or so at a time.

10. With an astounding speed of 35 mph (50 km/hr), the dragonfly beats out the hummingbird moth for the fastest-flying insect. No man-made airplane can do what the dragonfly can do. They can abruptly change direction in midair and can fly backwards or upside down. They can turn on a dime at sharp 90 degree angles. The Lord designed this flying machine with a long, tapered body to minimize drag from the wind. The delicate wings of the insect are also incredibly light but tough. Most insects have to move both wings together in concert, but the dragonfly's wings function independently. This acrobat flyer can move each wing up or down, backward or forward, to fly wherever he wants to go.

11. By eyesight, we can see fine definition in color, shape, size, and distances all at once. We can pick up on very slight differences between the distances and appearances of objects and people. Sight helps us to quickly assess the safety of a situation, and sight helps to coordinate our movements. Think about how hard it would be to eat a meal while sitting in the dark.

12. Evolution teaches that more complex systems developed more recently. Yet, evolutionists believe that the trilobite is a prehistoric creature that lived millions of years ago. Eyesight is the most sophisticated of all of God's creation. And the eyesight of the trilobite is even more sophisticated. This contradicts the evolutionary idea that complex systems developed later in history. Why would

the less complex systems like the trilobite's eyesight have evolved first and then gone extinct?

13. Steps in order include:
1. Many light rays will bounce off the things the eye is looking at.
2. Light rays enter the eye.
3. The light passes through a lens in the front of the eye.
4. The lens focuses the light rays on to the retina at the back of the eye.
5. The photoreceptors on the retina collect the data which will be transmitted to the brain (or the ganglia in some invertebrates).

FAITH LESSONS

1. 400 billion birds. 100,000 hairs. 700,000,000,000,000 hairs (700 trillion). Answers will vary.

2. Answers will vary.

CHAPTER 7, PART II

VOCABULARY

Hammer	A small bone transmitting sound, located in the middle ear
Frequency	A measurement of the highness or lowness of sound
Diematic behavior	Animal behavior or display meant to fool or startle other animals
Bombardier beetle	Animal with a very complicated defense mechanism, using an explosive technique
Vectors	Animals that transfer a disease from one organism to another
Pharynx	A tube connecting to the mouth meant to transfer food, sometimes called the throat
Gizzard	A muscular organ found in insects (and birds) meant to grind up food
Cochlea	A spiral cavity in the inner ear which transfers sound through neural pathways
Parasite	An organism that lives off of other animals or humans
Parthenogenesis	Reproduction from an egg or ovum without fertilization

Eardrum	A membrane in the middle ear which vibrates to sound
Bottom feeders	Aquatic animals which eat their food from the bottom of lakes or oceans
Esophagus	A muscular tube meant to transfer food into the stomach
Semicircular canals	Fluid-filled channels in the ear to help the body stay balanced (even in the dark)
Excretory tubules	Waste products from grasshoppers pass through these to the intestines
Hemolymph	Blood-like fluid found in most invertebrates
Olfactory system	God's design for smelling

COMPREHENSION QUESTIONS

1. a. The sound waves hit the eardrum (or the tympanic membrane). This membrane starts to vibrate.
b. The Lord attached a hammer on the other side of the membrane, and the vibration causes the hammer to move back and forth.
c. Like a complicated machine, the hammer moves another bone called the anvil, which moves a third bone called the stirrup.
d. The stirrup presses up against the cochlea. It's filled up with fluid and sealed up with a membrane. When the stirrup vibrates against the membrane, the fluid in the cochlea reacts by wave action. These waves are picked up by little hair cells which bend one way or another as the fluid passes over them.
e. The little hair cells release neurotransmitters (little packages of electrical energy) which transmit to the brain through the neural pathways. This translates the sound into an electrical signal that's passed on to the brain.

2. As you spin around on the merry-go-round, those fluids in your inner ear slosh against tiny strands of neurons. When you get off the merry-go-round, the fluid is still jiggling around. The neurons continue firing messages off to the brain, telling it that the body is still in motion. The brain is telling you that you are moving or that your surroundings are moving. You might even lose your balance and fall down because your brain is misinterpreting the message from the juices sloshing around in the semicircular canals.

3. The moth

4. Dolphins and rats

5. The pigeon

6. Snakes don't have ears. Instead, the Creator installed

a delicate little bone in the jaw of the animal. The bone vibrates to sounds coming from the ground or the air.

7. There are two reasons: The human nose contains 5-10 million olfactory receptor neurons, but dogs have 300 million of these neurons. Also, the human nose breathes in air and then breathes it out right away. But, dogs tuck away about 12% of the air breathed in. This works its way into a maze of bony caverns. This gives the dog's nose a chance to sort out all the chemicals (or smells) coming through.

8. It would be fair to say that a jellyfish is 100 times more intelligent than a plant. A roundworm with a pair of ganglia is 100 times more intelligent than a jellyfish. A dog or an ape would be a hundred times more intelligent than a roundworm. But, a human would be a million times more intelligent than a dog or an ape. God made these creatures with varying levels of intelligence. Nonetheless, all of these creations demonstrate God's limitless genius and command our praise.

9. The octopus is probably the smartest invertebrate created by God. He's equipped with 500 million neurons, most of which are in his arms. He has only 150 million in his brain. That's about the same number of neurons as dogs have, but it is only 0.5% of the number of neurons found in the human body.

10. The planarian can reproduce itself into two worms when it is cut in two pieces. Incredibly, even small pieces of the worm can grow back into another full-sized worm. This is called "reproduction by regeneration."

11. Most insects and other invertebrates reproduce with a male and a female animal each contributing a cell to conceive a new life. Most arthropods will lay eggs which hatch anywhere from two days to two months later.

12. The liver and reproductive organs of the puffer fish are extremely poisonous—a stronger poison than cyanide. An average of two people die each year from consuming puffer fish in Japan. There are also highly poisonous salamanders, as well as the poison dart frog and the Hawksbill sea turtles which are too dangerous to eat.

FAITH LESSONS

1. Answers will vary.

2. Answers will vary.

CHAPTER 8, PART I

COMPREHENSION QUESTIONS

1. Order of creatures using 1 to 6 from lowest to highest in the Creation order:
   5—Vertebrate animals (with hearts and lungs)
   2—Microbes
   4—Vertebrate animals (without hearts and lungs)
   3—Invertebrate animals
   6—Humans
   1—Plants

2. The five most common classes of vertebrates include fish, amphibians, reptiles, birds, and mammals. Typically, zoologists add two more classes to this list. The class Chondrichthyes includes sharks, rays, and chimeras, and the class Agnatha is made up of jawless fish.

3. Typically, vertebrates have brains and invertebrates have ganglia, which means vertebrates are smarter. They also have better sensory organs.

4. Dogs can learn 100 words. Humans learn 30,000 words. Humans can take care of creation. They can solve complex problems, treat medical problems, and build skyscrapers. They can use technology to convey information and move people from one place to another very quickly. Rats and monkeys don't manufacture cars. Humans are moral creatures. That means they have a moral conscience. They feel guilt when they disobey God's laws. Therefore, humans are concerned with atonement. They need to know that their sins have been paid for, that they are reconciled to God, and that they are in a right relationship with God.

5. Neanderthal man was a man. DNA confirmed it.

6. Lucy was an ape. Her toes were curved like most tree-dwelling apes. Her wrists were bent like knuckle-walking monkeys and apes. And, her shoulders looked exactly like modern apes'.

7. There are several reasons it is hard to believe that a fish turned into an amphibian or a reptile. The intermediate form where an animal is half-fish and half-amphibian would not be a biological advancement or serve as an advantage. It would be a hardship for the animal. This contradicts the basic theory of evolution. Also, there is no significant evidence of intermediate forms in the fossil layers that would mark these transitions from one kind of animal to another. The ultimate reason is that God created everything, all animals (each by their kind), in six days, according to Exodus 20:11.

8. A typical car is made of 30,000 parts. It takes about 200 moving parts to get the car to propel itself down the road. Compare that to the human body created by God. This has 30,000,000,000,000 unique parts. Within each of these cells, there are thousands of things going on at the same time. Every part of the body is a moving part. Some parts of the cell are making energy, some are making new proteins, some are involved in transportation and communication.

9. Epithelial tissue—Skin, hair follicles, and outside covering of bodily organs
    Muscle tissue—Muscles
    Connective tissue—Ligaments, tendons, skin, bones, fat, and blood
    Nervous tissue—Nerves, brain, and spinal cord

10. There are approximately 30 trillion cells in the body.
    There are 650-840 muscles in the body.
    There are 200 kinds of cells in the body.
    The heart pumps 2,500 gallons of blood in 24 hours.
    There are 2 trillion white blood cells.

11. When you use your hands over and over again for heavy work, your body feels the extra pressure. Over time, the epidermal cells produce even more cells in that area, thickening the skin into a callus. This is one more way the skin protects the body from injury. Praise God for His wise provision for the body!
    If the skin is subject to too much pressure, friction, or heat over a short time, a blister forms. This can happen if you take a long hike in shoes that rub against your feet. The dermis separates from the epidermis and fluid gets in between, causing the blister.

12. Skin provides a wonderful protective covering for the body. Skin blocks bacteria and dangerous chemicals from getting inside your body. When you go swimming or when you climb into a bathtub, your skin keeps water from soaking your muscles and organs. Skin makes for a good waterproof raincoat! Your skin can take a lot of abuse. When you fall, the rest of your body is protected from injury.

VOCABULARY

Microvilli	Finger-like protrusions in the intestines that collect food
Nerve cells	Passes on electrical signals to the brain
Storage granule organelles	Little storage barrels holding insulin
Chondrichthyes	Sharks, rays, and chimeras

Cardiac muscles	Muscles that work automatically and control the heart
Voluntary muscle	A muscle that contracts when you want it to
Callus	Epidermis forms extra layers over time in a particular area of the hands or feet that are used a lot
Melanoma	Serious form of skin cancer
Connective tissue	The tissue that holds the body together
Epidermis	The part of the skin you see
Dermis	The layer of skin just underneath your outer skin
Pancreas	Produces insulin to regulate sugar in the body
Subcutaneous layer	The innermost part of the skin
Agnatha	Jawless fish
Blister	When fluid gets between the dermis and epidermis
Epithelial tissue	Tissue meant to confine the body and protect the body and its organs
Smooth muscles	Involuntary muscles used for the digestive tract, respiratory tract, or urinary tract
Eukaryotic cells	Cells that contain membrane-bound organelles
Red blood cells	Carries oxygen around the body
Masseter	Jaw muscle, the strongest in the body

FAITH LESSONS

1. Answers may vary. God demonstrates His power by making something that is dead to live. Where there was nothing but dead cells or dry bones, He makes sinews, flesh, and skin to cover the bones. But, most importantly He breathes the breath of life back into them, and the bodies start to live and move again. This is a picture of the spiritual resurrections that happen when the Holy Spirit breathes new life into us.

2. Answers may vary.

3. Answers may vary. We differ from animals in our knowledge and moral character. We have moral consciences. We think more as God thinks, something animals cannot do. Evolutionists try to avoid God's judgment by making us essentially equal to animals. Thus, they try to exempt us from being moral creatures, created in the image of God with moral responsibility

to God. They do this because they do not want to face His judgment, and they are trying to pacify their own consciences.

CHAPTER 8, PART II

VOCABULARY

Prolactin	A hormone used for production of a mother's milk
Reflexes	Actions initiated by the spinal cord
Axon	A pathway through the neuron
Spinal cord	Concentrated collection of neuron pathways running up the center of the back
Endocrine system	Glands regulating body temperature, blood pressure, metabolism, etc.
Pupil	Dark spot in eye allows light to enter
Dendrites	Each neuron has 128 of them
Retina	Forms the image using neurons
Cardiovascular system	Heart and blood vessels
Cornea	Controls and focuses light
Respiratory system	Breathing
Iris	Regulates the size of the pupil
Synapse	Junction between two nerve cells
Neurotransmitters	Vesicles that carry the signal across the synapses
Peripheral nervous system	Ears and eyes
Sclera	The white of the eye

COMPREHENSION QUESTIONS

1. Water molecules, protein molecules, and fat molecules
   Cells
   Tissues
   Organs
   Your body

2. 78-100 organs

3. $180 billion compared to $20 billion

4. A camera lens is a rigid glass, and the lens has to move mechanically to keep things in focus. The eye lens is flexible, and muscles around the eye quickly adjust the lens so everything stays in focus all the time. With optimum vision, the human eye is about the same as a 52 megapixel camera. One picture taken with a 52 megapixel camera would take about 15 MB of memory. Now, some eyes can be trained to pick up 255 frames per second. That would amount to about 4 GB per second of information transferred to the brain. Just two minutes of eyesight would fill up your hard drive on a laptop computer. That's how much information your eyes are processing all day long! The retina can also adjust to varying amounts of light, whereas the camera film can't do that.

5. About 500,000 neurons were designed to detect surface conditions by determining whether they are soft, hard, rough, or silky. Another 200,000 of these neurons are sensitive to temperature. If your skin could not detect heat, you would burn your fingers or other parts of your body over and over again (without knowing it).

6. Dopamine, adrenaline, and endorphins.

7. 0.015 seconds

8. The nerves on your hand can pick up the difference between a smooth pane of glass and a 0.0004 inch scratch in the glass. That's 1/10 the size of what you can see with the naked eye.

9. There is the short term memory (where five to seven facts or numbers can be remembered for a few seconds). There is also the long-term memory. There is a declarative memory of names, numbers, and facts. Then, there is also non-declarative memory where we learn to do things by habitual practice. There are also "flashbulb" memories where we can remember many details of some memorable event.

FAITH LESSONS

Answers may vary.

CHAPTER 9, PART I

COMPREHENSION QUESTIONS

1. Food, water, and air to breathe.

2. The Lord designed the mouth to be quite versatile, so it can eat, chew, taste, speak, breathe, cough, sneeze and blow.

3. You can eat and breathe at the same time because food

and air take different paths after passing through the pharynx. Air flows from your pharynx, through your larynx, and into your lungs, while food is guided from your pharynx into your esophagus.

4. First, it filters out germs that make it into the nasal cavity. Bacteria and viruses breathed into the nose get stuck in a thin layer of sticky mucus. Then, tiny cilia hairs sweep the mucus with all the germs down into your throat.
Please replace this paragraph with the following from the textbook:
The second way your nose benefits your bodily health is by treating the air as it enters your lungs. There are blood vessels running very close to the surface of your nose which are designed to warm up the air as it enters the nasal cavity. Since they are so close to the surface, you can have nose bleeds if your nose is too dry. Your lungs appreciate the warm, moist air coming in through your nose rather than the cold, dry air coming through your mouth when you're outdoors in cold weather. Your lungs need to stay moist.
The third benefit of the nose is the sneeze, ridding the body of any invasion of foreign materials like dust, smoke, and microbes.

5. When you swallow, the food passes through the pharynx, where the epiglottis flap closes over the larynx which leads to the lungs. This prevents food from getting into the larynx.

6. When you breathe, the glottis is wide open. But when you talk, the glottis opens only a little bit, making the vocal cords vibrate.

7. Answers may vary slightly.
Step 1—Air enters the nose or mouth
Step 2—Air passes through the larynx and the windpipe
Step 3—Air passes through one of the two branches into the two lungs
Step 4—Air passes through the sub-branches and the bronchioles
Step 5—Air ends up in the alveoli sacs, and oxygen is passed into the blood stream.
Step 6—Carbon dioxide from the body is passed into the air in the alveoli sacs.
Step 7—The air is exhaled back through the bronchioles, into the windpipe, through the larynx, and out through the nose or mouth.

8. Pray, apply five back blows, and do the Heimlich maneuver.

9. Humans are capable of producing a huge range of vocal sounds by adjusting air flow through the mouth and nose. Singers learn how to position their mouths, control air by using the diaphragm muscle, and adjust the vocal cords to produce amazing, beautiful performances.

10. 21%—16.4% = 3.6% (which is about 17% of the oxygen breathed in)

11. About a gallon (4-5 L).

12. The yellowish top layer is the blood plasma. A very thin middle layer contains white blood cells and platelets. Then, the bottom layer contains red blood cells.

13. There are billions of activities going on even when you are asleep. It takes energy to breathe. It takes energy for your heart to beat. Oxygen is a fuel that helps turn food into energy in every corner of your body. Your brain uses about 20% of the total oxygen intake. The busy brain cells start dying within 4-5 minutes of losing access to oxygen. You would die within about 10 minutes without oxygen.

VOCABULARY

Erythrocytes	Vehicles carrying oxygen to the body
Hemoglobin	The iron-rich part of the blood that makes it look red
Vocal cords	Surround the glottis; vibrates to makes sounds
Right atrium	Deoxygenated blood comes back into this section of the heart
Glottis	The larynx, where choking occurs
Hyperventilation	Exhaling more air than the lungs are inhaling
Left atrium	Blood comes back into the heart from the lungs into this section of the heart
Tracheotomy	A hole cut by a doctor in the throat to enable a choking victim to breathe
AV node	The backup node to keep the heart going at a regular pulse
Aorta	The main artery leaving the heart
Diaphragm muscle	The muscle in the body used to breathe
Aspiration	When water or food makes it into your lungs
Arteries	The blood vessels carrying oxygenated blood throughout the body
Centrifuge	An instrument used to separate out the different components of the blood
Bronchioles	30,000 of these little tubes are in the lungs

Sinoatrial node	The part of the heart that keeps the pulse
Veins	The blood vessels returning the deoxygenated blood to the heart
Anitgen	Protein coating on red blood cells to stimulate immune response
Transfusion	Providing replacement blood for a patient who has lost blood
Leukocytes	Hunts and destroys bad germs in the body
Blood plasma	Keeps blood at the right consistency and transports food throughout the body

Hemorrhagic stroke	Artery develops a leak
Heart attack	When the heart stops due to problems with blood flow or other issues
Liver	Organ filters dirt and unusable stuff from the blood
Hydrochloric acid	Digestive fluids contain this
Salivary glands	Produces liquid to moisten food as you chew it

FAITH LESSONS

1. Christ, the Son of God created all things.
   They continue to exist in Christ.
   Answers will vary. Breathing, health of the body, etc.

2. Singing, blessing others, and speaking of God's attributes and His righteous laws.

CHAPTER 9, PART II

VOCABULARY

Aneurysm	A bulge in the wall of the artery
Ischemic stroke	A blockage in the main artery in the brain
Stethoscope	Instrument used to listen for heart murmurs and other problems
Atherosclerosis	Cholesterol and calcium buildup in the arteries
Alimentary canal	Long tube taking food through the digestive process
Systolic pressure	Measures blood pressure as the heart contracts and is represented by the higher number in the reading
Kidneys	Organ that filters out unusable stuff from blood and sends it into the bladder as urine
Diastolic pressure	Measures blood pressure between heartbeats and is represented by the lower number in the reading
Anticoagulants	Blood thinner—helps blood to flow
Protease enzyme	Breaks down proteins

COMPREHENSION QUESTIONS

1. Coronary heart disease. 15.5% of deaths. It is caused by a buildup of fatty substances or calcium in the arteries.

2. Strokes. 11% of all deaths. It is caused by clots in the blood.

3. F—Face: Ask the person to smile. Does one side of the face droop?
   A—Arms: Ask the person to raise both arms. Does one arm drift downward?
   S—Speech: Ask the person to repeat a simple phrase. Is the speech slurred or strange?
   T—Time: If you see any of these signs, call 9-1-1 right away.

4. It could break loose and clog up your lungs or block your heart.

5. Half an hour per day

6. 3 glasses of milk (300 mg)
   2 slices of cheese (800 mg)
   4 slices of bread (600 mg)
   1 cheeseburger (1000 mg)
   1 cup of baked beans (1000 mg)
   3,700 mg—too much sodium.
   3 glasses of milk (300 mg)
   4 slices of bread (600 mg)
   1 apple (130 mg)
   1 slice of cheese (400 mg)
   1 can of beef stew (1000 mg)
   2,430 mg—too much sodium.
   3 glasses of milk (300 mg)
   4 slices of bread (600 mg)
   1 apple (130 mg)
   1 cheeseburger (1000 mg)
   1 bag of potato chips (170 mg)
   2,200 mg—less than maximum daily recommended limit for sodium.

7. Twenty teeth for children, and 32 for adults

8. The limpet

9. Dirt and unusable foods go into the stomach and then into the small intestine. The blood picks up the dirt and passes it through the liver. From here it is moved into the intestines and then passed out as a bowel movement.

10. Half an ounce of caffeine would be deadly. A triple shot contains about 225 mg, so it would take about 62 of these drinks to kill you. About three cherry pits could kill you.

11. Acids will break down the enamel covering your teeth. Sugar is rough on teeth because the sugar feeds the bacteria already hanging out on your teeth, and that's what produces the harmful acids.

FAITH LESSONS

1. You want to take care of your physical heart because heart disease is the most deadly disease known to man. And, we are supposed to do all within our means to preserve our own lives and the lives of others.
You want to take care of your invisible/spiritual heart because "out of it spring the issues of life."

2. The dirt goes into the stomach and is expelled (through the intestines). No, the dirt does not defile a man. Here is what defiles a man: evil thoughts, murder, adultery, sexual immorality, theft, false witness, and slander.

CHAPTER 10, PART I

COMPREHENSION QUESTIONS

1. Thermostats control the temperature in a house. Fuel injection systems in cars control the mix of air and gas.

2. Water, glucose, temperature, blood pressure, minerals, and growth.

3. Like mRNA, hormones give instructions to cells and body parts.

4. Hormones act as a switch on specific cells. Certain hormones attach to certain cells equipped with uniquely-fitted receptors. Once the hormone attaches, that cell will either increase or decrease specific activities in the cell. Since there are billions of hormones attaching to billions of receptors, this regulates entire systems in the body.

5. Step 1—The nervous system lets the hypothalamus know the body is getting too warm.
Step 2—The hypothalamus releases hormones to instruct the body to cool itself down.

Step 3—Hormones signal the blood vessels near the surface of the skin to expand, increasing blood flow. The blood carries your body heat to the surface, where the heat is convected into the surrounding air. Also, sweat glands begin to operate, forming moisture on the surface of your skin. As air moves across your body, the moisture evaporates, creating a cooling effect on your body.

6. When the body detects a new antigen enemy, the B white blood cells start working on a new antibody. While this happens, the person might get sick for a while. The antibody globs on to the enemy antigen, crippling it. With the antibody hanging on to the outside of the enemy cell, it won't be able to reproduce or move around the body.

7. Vaccines contain an antigen less severe but similar to the virus, which programs the body to create an antibody to destroy it. When and if a child should come upon the real virus later on, the body would have the antibodies ready to destroy the germ.

8. Lizard tails, amphibian jaws, and the endometrium in a mother's womb

9. The steps are in this order:
1. The male and female cells join to make a new cell, a new human life.
2. The zygote becomes two cells by mitosis.
3. The zygote makes its way down the fallopian tubes.
4. The zygote attaches itself to the mother's womb.

10. Every cell has a chromosome pair that determines gender. The XX chromosome pair is a girl. The XY chromosome pair is a boy.

11. a. Boys get more of a hormone called testosterone. Girls get more of the hormones called estrogen and progesterone.
b. Boys tend to convert their food into muscle. God made the bodies of girls to convert more food into fat, which will help them bear children.
c. Boys get more red blood cells, and girls get more white blood cells.

VOCABULARY

Hyperglycemia	High blood sugar
Progesterone	Female hormone that gets fluids ready to nourish the new baby in the womb
Epinephrine	Hormone produced by adrenal gland
Glands	Chemical factories that make hormones

Cell-mediated immunity	When white blood cells shoot bullets at bad bacteria, fungi, or cancer cells
Thymus gland	Makes white blood cells
Hormones	Chemicals that carry instructions to various parts of the body
Endocrine system	Controls the body's temperature, minerals, sugar content, water content, etc.
Complement response	The immune response that destroys the invader cells by eating them or by attaching themselves to them
Hypothalamus gland	Controls the body's temperature
Phagocytes	These will eat the invader cells
Humoral immune response	When an antibody globs on to the outside of an enemy cell
Zygote	When a human baby is only one cell
Antigen	Foreign invader stimulating an immune response from the body
Estrogen	The hormone that thickens the blood-rich tissue lining the surface of the womb
Pituitary gland	The master gland, producing at least 10 hormones, including your growth hormone
Poliomyelitis	A virus that used to kill thousands of children
Hypoglycemia	Low blood sugar
Autoimmune diseases	The body's immune system attacks normal cells
Homeostasis	The right balance for the body
Testosterone	Male hormone that grows boy-like features in a boy
Fimbriae	Hair-like things that coax the newly-formed baby up the fallopian tube
Zona pellucida	The outside of the human cell hardens to protect the new baby

FAITH LESSONS

1. God brought the diseases. The Lord heals our diseases. And God shows mercy by providing an immune system to attack disease in the bodies of all human beings (even after man fell into sin).

2. The human is of great value, much more than an animal. The human has an eternal soul, and he or she has been made in the image of God. God has placed value upon us. That is why we are valuable.

CHAPTER 10, PART II

VOCABULARY

Myelin	Covering of nerve cells in the brain which speeds up the flow of information and learning for the baby
Anesthesia	Making patients unconscious so they don't feel pain during surgery
Uterus	Scientific word for "womb"
Bone marrow	The center of a bone where red blood cells are made
Voluntary muscles	Skeletal muscles that move when we make the conscious decision to make them move
Endometrium	Blood-rich layer of tissue lining the mother's womb
Involuntary muscles	Muscles that function without our thinking about it
Abortion	Ending a baby's life while it is still in the womb
Placenta	An organ forming inside the mother's womb, which transfers oxygen and food to the baby
C-section	A surgery where doctors take the baby from the mother's womb
Arthritis	The breakdown of cartilage causes pain when bone rubs against bone
Umbilical cord	Contains tubes connecting the baby's stomach to the placenta

COMPREHENSION QUESTIONS

1. Nine months

2. By womb milk secreted by glands in the uterus. It is a mix of glucose and glycoproteins.
   By blood transferred from the placenta.

3. The umbilical cord contains two arteries which take blood from the baby to the mother's body. These arteries carry waste products which get transferred to the mother and are eliminated in the mother's system. The cord also contains one vein which brings nutrition and oxygen into the baby's body.

4. Mixing blood could be fatal if the mother's blood type

and the infant's blood type are different.

5. Weeks 1-2—hair width
    Week 3—size of a period
    Week 4—size of a poppy seed
    Week 5—size of a shirt button
    Week 6—size of a lentil bean
    Week 7—size of two lentil beans
    Week 9—size of a grape
    Week 12—size of a lime
    Week 16—4.5 inches long

6. Head down

7. Cleanliness standards in hospitals, c-sections and anesthesia, and better diets for moms

8. Bone is made up of living cells, minerals like calcium and phosphorus, and blood vessels. There are also nerves in the bones. That's why it's so painful when you break a bone. Also, blood runs through the bone, providing ongoing oxygen and nourishment to the cells. Inside some of your bones runs a long narrow tube. This contains bone marrow where red blood cells are produced.

9. The hinge joint is what you get for your knees and elbows. Your spine uses gliding joints. Your hips have ball-and-socket joints, while your forearm uses the pivot joint so you can twist your arms this way and that way. The skull also has fused joints, which do not allow any movement.

10. Five differences between the skeleton/structure of humans and apes:
    God gave humans super strong big toes. Apes use their thumbs to grip things, but it doesn't help them to walk. God pieced 26 uniquely-shaped bones together in each foot, forming a nice arch. The human foot is very flexible as well, so pressure can be shifted between the right foot and the left foot when walking. To help with your balance, the foot is shaped like a tripod with three points of contact—one behind the big toe, one behind the smallest toe, and one at the heel. Apes and monkeys are flat footed, which makes it harder for them to stay balanced. And they certainly cannot run on two feet. The Lord also made human legs much longer than ape legs (in proportion to the rest of the body). This helps humans to walk long distances without too much trouble.
    Humans can also stand on two legs for a long time because the Creator gave them a knee joint that locks in place. An ape would topple over in a few seconds or minutes.
    Also, apes are inefficient and clumsy when they run. They tend to waddle using a swaying, back-and-forth motion. That's because their femur (leg) bones are separated by quite a distance from the centerline of their torsos. Since

God made man with femur bones that angle inwards, he has much better balance.

11. The body will send cartilage-like material into the break. This seeps into the crack like glue. Then, the body adds a little more calcium and phosphorus to it so the patch will turn into hard bone.

12. The human is extremely skillful with his hands. These are designed for a full range of movements.
    A child can hold a pencil with a "tripod grip." It is a very complicated method, requiring the coordination of the thumb, the index finger, and the middle finger. Animals are too clumsy and they could never hold a pencil that way. Also, the motor cortex of the human brain is in charge of the body's movements. About 25% of this part of the brain is used to control hand movement.

13. The muscles in your face allow you a range of 10,000 expressions! Whereas God gave humans 50 facial muscles, gorillas only have 30. But none of them are for making facial expressions.

14. The humble trilobite had the most excellent eyesight. The opossum is blessed with an opposable thumb. And the Creator provided the koala bear with human-like fingerprints. Bats are equipped with the most amazing system of echolocation, and salamanders get their own red blood cells.

15. Most of the babies conceived are killed by abortion and abortifacient methods and drugs.

FAITH LESSONS

1. He was trusting God and hoping in God. The child must have been a personality in that he was in relationship with God while still a tiny baby. Only personalities (real persons) can be in relationship with each other.

2. Answers may vary some. God forbids murder. The Child must have had a personality because He was in relationship with God while still a tiny baby. Only real persons have personalities and can be in relationship with each other.

3. God's only begotten Son took on human flesh for Himself. For nine months, Jesus was growing in Mary's womb. His body had our DNA, our proteins, our myosin, our white blood cells, and our collagen. With this same body, He died on the cross for our sins. And then, He rose again with a resurrected body such that the nail prints were still visible. From this we learn that Jesus does not despise human flesh, but honored us by taking upon Himself this body. We also learn of His humility and His love for us, to suffer as He did for us on the cross.

4. Answers will vary.

ANSWER KEY

FINAL EXAM

TRUE OR FALSE

1. True
2. False
3. False
4. True
5. False
6. True
7. False
8. True
9. True
10. False

MATCHING

Xylem	Used for bringing minerals and water up into the plant
Phloem	Used for bringing sugar and nutrition down into the roots of a plant
Parasites	Hurtful protozoa that live off the host at the expense of the health of the host
Chlorophyll	Keeps leaves green
Pistil	Part of plant that contains female gametes
Pancreas	Organ in the body producing insulin
Veins	Carries blood filled with carbon dioxide back to the heart
Vertebrates	Animals with backbones
Antigen	Something in the body stirring up the body's immune response
Placenta	Provides food and oxygen through blood while the baby is in his/her mother's womb

SHORT ANSWER

1. Producers—Plants
   Consumers—Carnivores, omnivores, herbivores
   Decomposers—Bacteria, fungi

2. Flagellum motor, clotting

3. Humans, Animals with the breath of life, animals without the breath of life, and plants

4. Colds, flu, HIV/AIDS, COVID-19, polio, rabies, hepatitis, measles, mumps, rabies, smallpox, warts

5. Cholera, leprosy, tuberculosis, plague, syphilis, food poisoning, meningitis, pneumonia, anthrax

6. Red blood cells, white blood cells, platelets

7. 46